Idle Women on the Water

A brick throwin', hijab-wearin'
hairy-legged, space takin' odyssey

For every woman

Idle Women on the Water

A brick throwin', hijab-wearin'
hairy-legged, space takin' odyssey

Candice Purwin

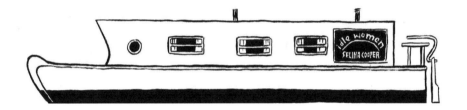

Published by Idle Women

Published by Idle Women 2020

Copyright © Candice Purwin and Idle Women

Candice Purwin and Idle Women collectively assert their moral rights under the Copyright, Designs and Patents Act 1988 to be identified as the author, commissioner and producer of this work.

First published in Great Britain in 2020 by Idle Women

Idle Women, CIC 09796415
www.idlewomen.org

A CIP catalogue record for this book is available from the British Library

ISBN 978-1-5272-6888-3

Edited by Janette Scott
Publication design by O-SB Design

The front and end matter of this publication uses the Ronnia font, designed by Veronika Burian and José Scaglione. Veronika Burian is involved with Alphabettes.org, a showcase for work and research on lettering, typography, and type design by women.

Printed and bound in Great Britain by Principal Colour

Foreword

There are a number of stories about the start of Idle Women. This one is told by Candice Purwin and documents our first project, *On the Water*, which amongst many other things, included the design, build and navigation of a narrowboat through Lancashire, West Yorkshire and Merseyside between 2015–2017.

We conceived Idle Women to pursue adventure, autonomy and artistic independence, and to make a space for all women to belong equally. A revolution on the canals seemed as good a place to begin as any, and the decision to build a boat and start on the water felt just about possible. Following a revelation that began in a bathtub in Finsbury Park, London, in 2015, we left our jobs, gave up our homes and gambled all that we had on securing funding to set up what was intended to be a one-off project. We didn't know then that this project would alter the course of our lives, and how far it would take us.

Before Candice (aka the 'Beast') takes up her story, with the help of arts pioneer Laurie Peake, we moved to Lancashire and sowed seeds for six months. We followed introductions, held events in cafes, supermarkets, abandoned mills, community centres and parks, met women, and invited artists to join us from far and wide. In those early beginnings, Salma Saleh picked up a flyer and called to invite us to meet women at a Humraaz coffee morning. It was one of the most important calls we received.

With Humraaz and the team at muf architecture/art, we conceived the design of the women's narrowboat in Blackburn. Tracing outlines on tow paths, moving furniture around to fit into tiny spaces whilst holding babies, and cooking omelettes on camping stoves, we got our heads collectively around what a boat built by women could be.

In Winter we commissioned the steel work for the boat, and in freezing conditions we lined and built the interior, painted the outside, and created the *Selina Cooper*. She launched on International Women's Day in 2016 in Burnley, and welcomed our first artist Martina Mullaney, her 7-year old daughter, and their dog aboard for the first 3-month residency. The Beast joined us for the first time on the morning of the community launch, nine months after that fateful bath...

Idle Women is an act of love. *On the Water* was the beginning of our journey to create space to belong. Nothing about either of these things is pretty or nice.

Rachel Anderson and Cis O'Boyle

Contents

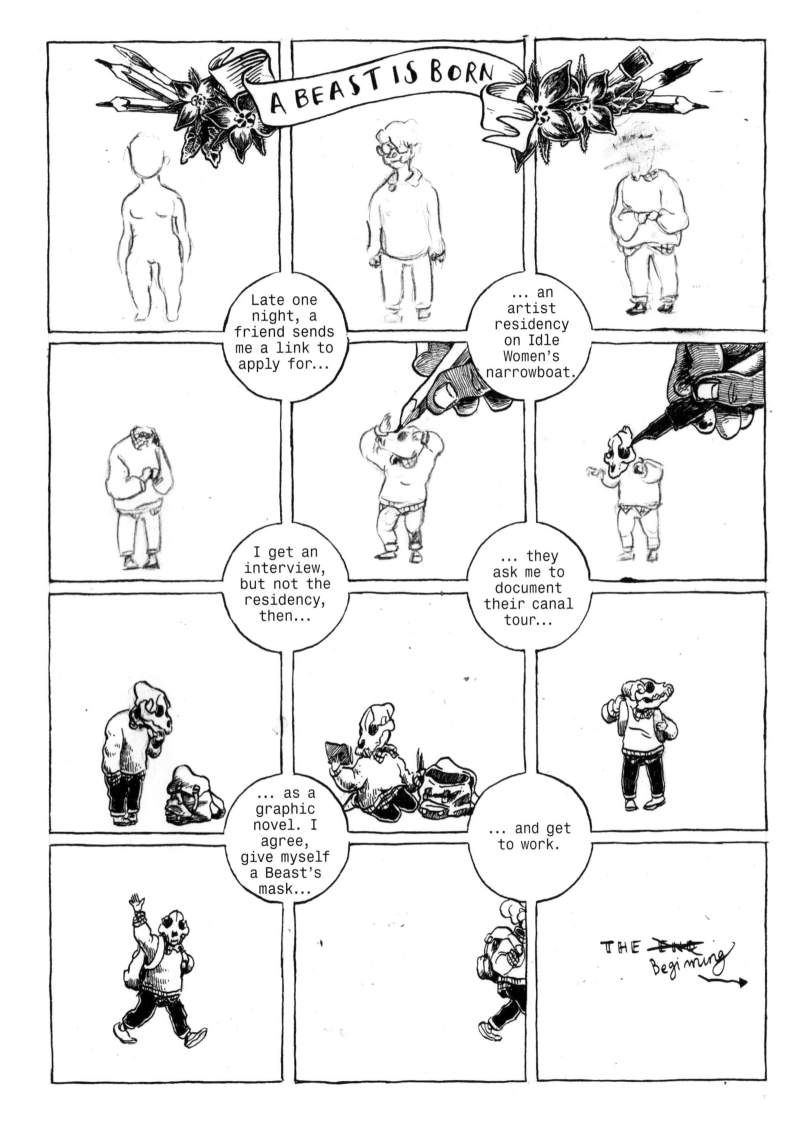

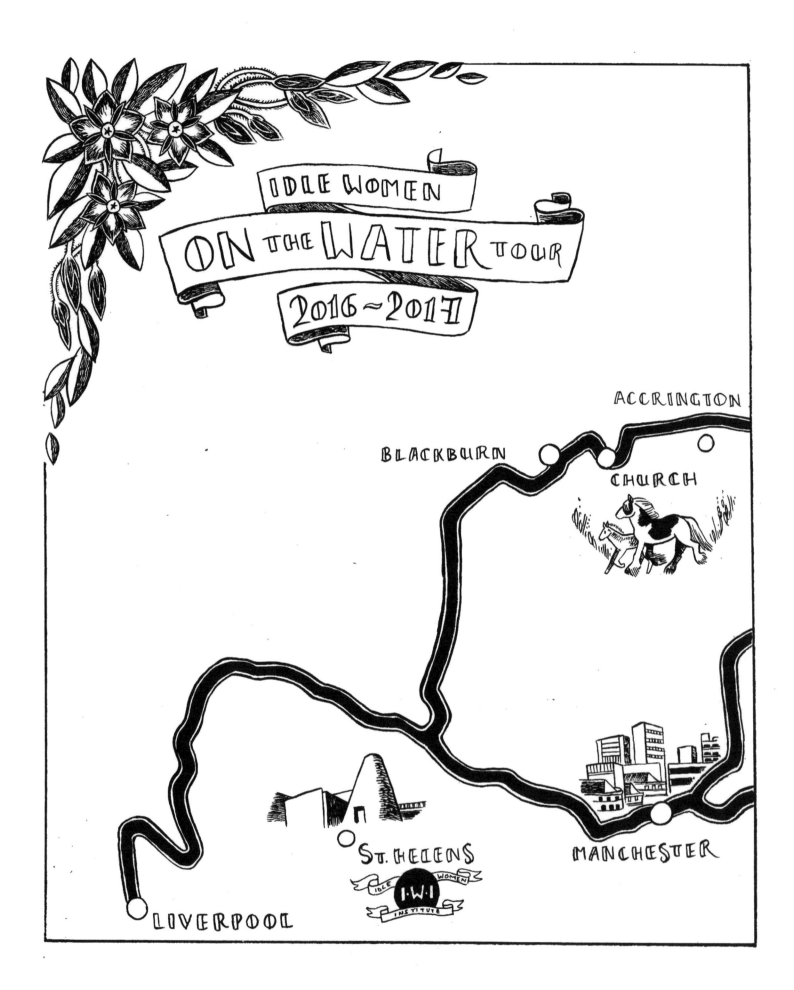

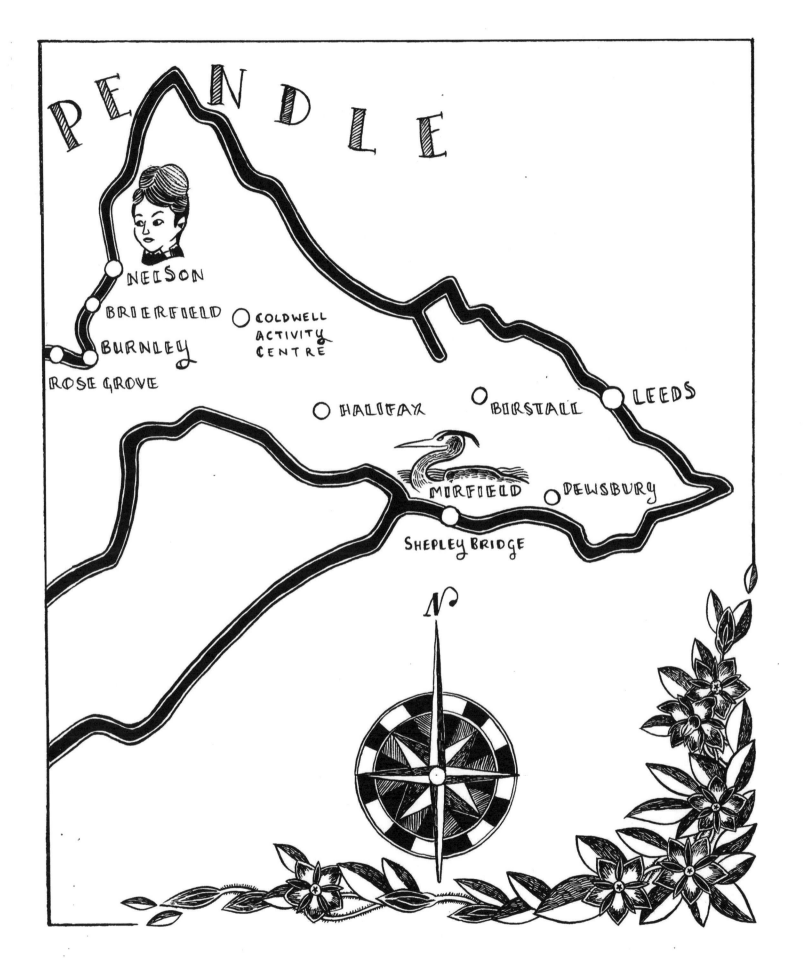

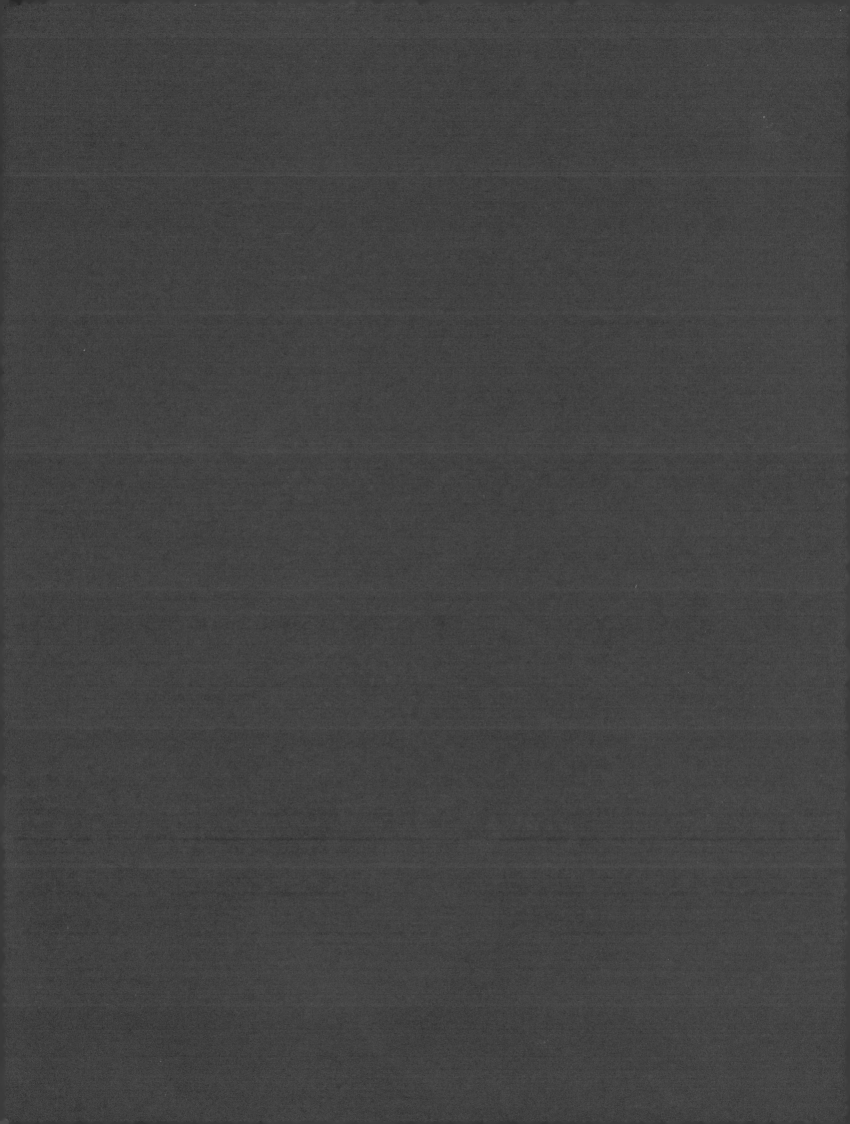

SPRING 2016

ROSE GROVE, LANGASHIRE

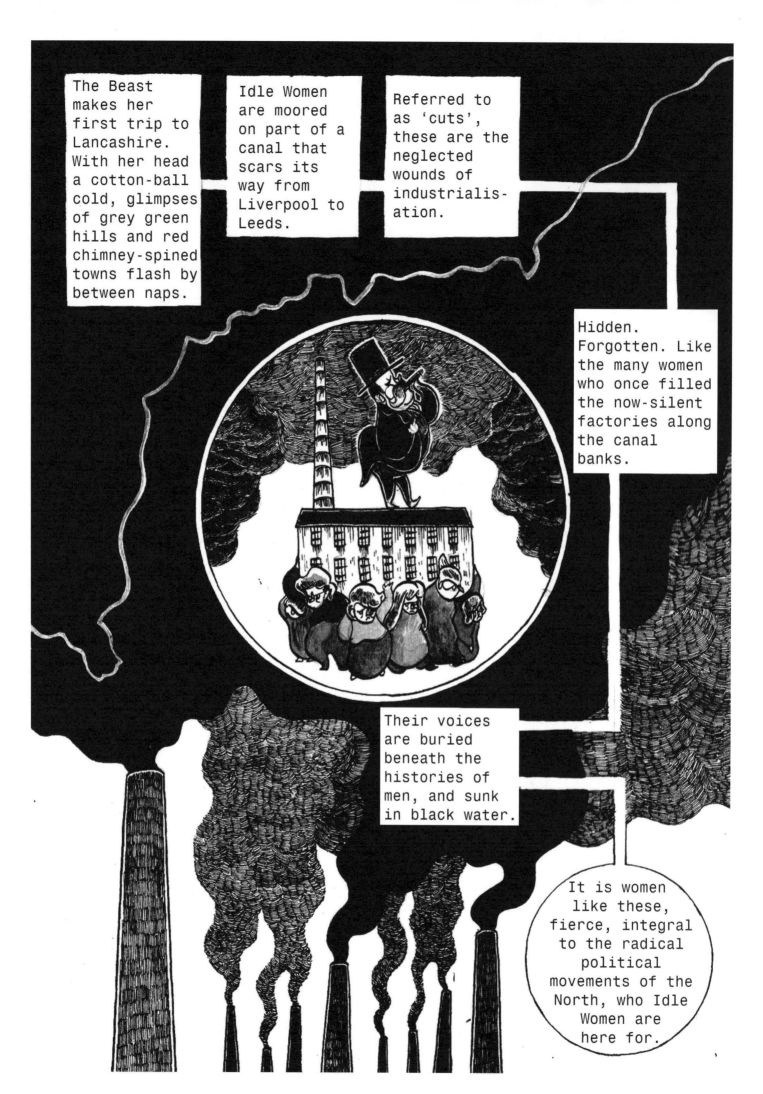

The Beast makes her first trip to Lancashire. With her head a cotton-ball cold, glimpses of grey green hills and red chimney-spined towns flash by between naps.

Idle Women are moored on part of a canal that scars its way from Liverpool to Leeds.

Referred to as 'cuts', these are the neglected wounds of industrialis-ation.

Hidden. Forgotten. Like the many women who once filled the now-silent factories along the canal banks.

Their voices are buried beneath the histories of men, and sunk in black water.

It is women like these, fierce, integral to the radical political movements of the North, who Idle Women are here for.

The women's suffrage movement was born in Lancashire and Cheshire in the late 1800s. The more infamous

suffragettes who scared up London in the early 20th century, were a middle class splinter group looking for the vote.

In contrast, suffrage in the North focused on bettering factory workers' immediate living and working conditions.

The vote was an abstract solution to the poverty, employer abuse and violence that was everyday life.

These women fought a slow and powerful struggle against a system intent on disenfranchising the working class.

Amongst the few names that have survived the wilful erosion of their actions, is that of Selina Cooper.

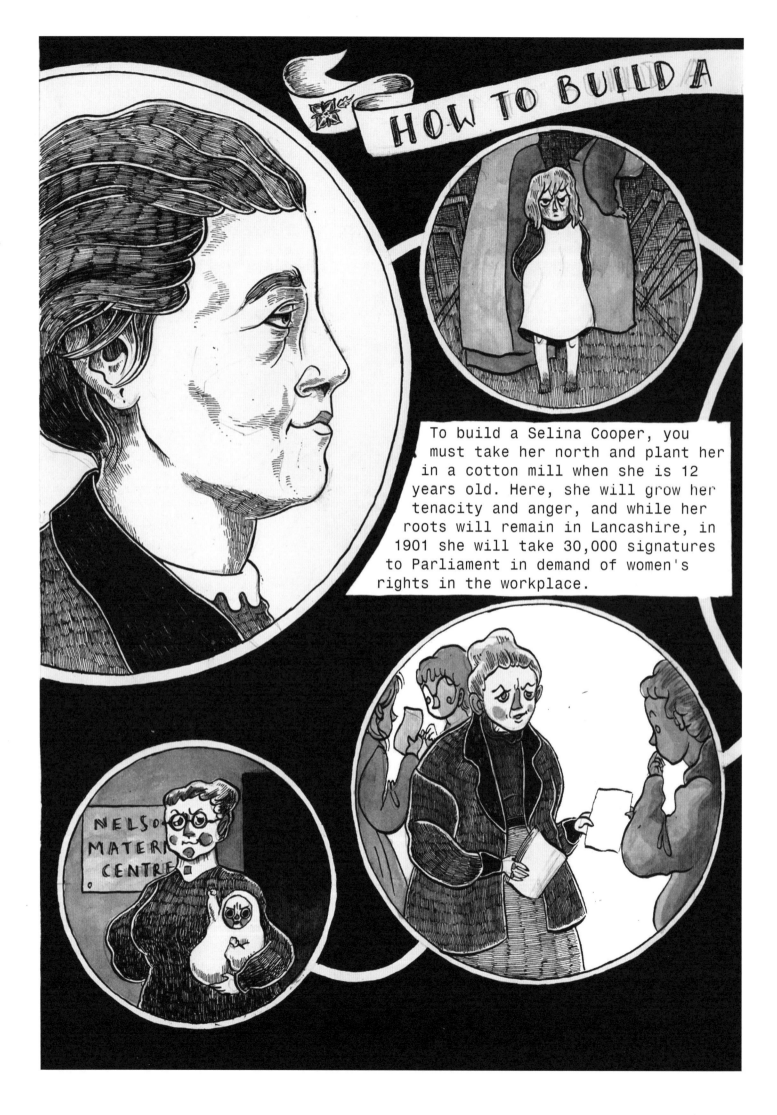

18

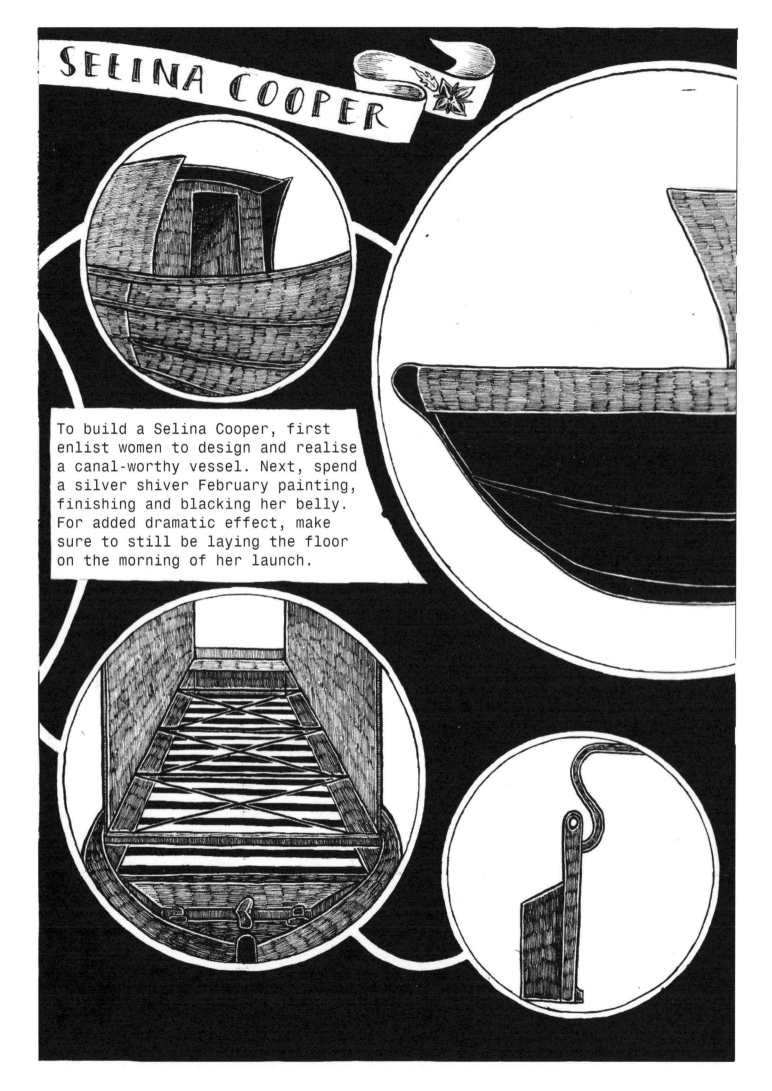

SELINA COOPER

To build a Selina Cooper, first enlist women to design and realise a canal-worthy vessel. Next, spend a silver shiver February painting, finishing and blacking her belly. For added dramatic effect, make sure to still be laying the floor on the morning of her launch.

19

Selina Cooper does not have an engine, so in order to traverse the slow northern waterways she relies on her sister vessel, the Adelaide Norris.

Adelaide Norris is named for the fictional Black lesbian activist whose death in prison sparks a revolution in Lizzie Borden's classic feminist film, 'Born in Flames.'

The boats were given these names to remind us that they are not passive spaces.

When Rachel Anderson, one of Idle Women's caretakers is told Selina 'isn't very pretty', she says 'We didn't want her to be pretty...'

'...we would have covered her

...in barbed wire if we could.'

In an old factory in Mill Hill, Blackburn, there is a room filled with orange plastic chairs.

The chairs have soft cushion covers that invite you to sit, and fluorescent light glistens over the slick laminated surfaces of pictures protesting against acid attacks, domestic violence, and poor working conditions for women.

Idle Women are here for a conference. An exchange of ideas, poetry translated as it's recited, and talks by women about the things happening outside that room, where the smell of snow hangs heavy in the air. The seismic shifts stirred by the words inside are at odds with the polystyrene drop ceiling, worn carpet and ex-office chic of the room.

The factory building is owned by Khushi who runs the organisation, Fair For All.

Khushi is one of a few local women Cis and Rachel have been able to connect with since coming to Lancashire.

The Beast watches those present speak, and if her head hadn't been a mucus-mess of cold-fever she's sure she would have been a better documentarian and recorded people's names and faces. As it is, her one vivid memory is:

One woman gets up to read a poem in Urdu.

Another gets up to translate.

And together they conjure a kaleidoscopic galaxy of pictures and sounds, exploding from abstraction into coloured images and back again with the flick of a tongue.

Rachel has been invited to talk about Idle Women and Cis O'Boyle, the project's other caretaker, would have been here too if she wasn't frantically varnishing Selina Cooper's floor in readiness for tomorrow's community launch.

Rachel begins by talking about the boat and the 'On the Water' canal tour. Then someone asks about 'Blood Moon Gossip', Idle Women's event of the previous Winter.

There was a time when the word 'gossip' had simply been a collective noun for a group of women who were friends.

Then, from the 17th century onwards as the witch hunts raged, gatherings of women began to raise suspicion and were even feared, and the word 'gossip' acquired derogatory connotations.

The Blood Moon Gossip was an attempt to reclaim the term as one of solidarity and power, but as the Beast listens to Rachel talk she feels the word 'witch' is also beginning to take on a new meaning.

  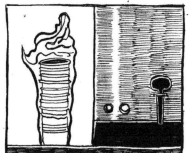 

Before the revelation can sink in too deeply though, it's lunchtime. If it had been up to the ailing Beast she would have sat under a table and fallen asleep, but she had to pretend she was normal and well.

The small cohort heap food on their plates from great steaming pots, and find places at the table. The Beast sits opposite a teenage girl Raffi, and her mother, Parveen.

Raffi is seventeen and has just won a scholarship to study engineering aboard a ship in the Black Sea. She is very excited. Parveen is clearly incredibly proud, and has high hopes that her youngest child will be the one who goes to Oxford.

Over burnt instant coffee in small plastic cups, Raffi goes on to rave about her mother's own mathematical talent. She is very aware of the advantages she has that were unavailable to her mum. And she has every intention of taking them.

(Meanwhile... ...the Beast can hear...

...a woman talk about how ill-equipped her community is to help...

...with her daughter's eating disorder.)

JUST ANOTHER · SATURDAY NIGHT

DO YOU HAVE ANY ANIMALS IN THERE?

While Rachel, the Beast, and friend and trustee of Idle Women, Ray, have had their spirits raised by the conference, Cis has been holding the fort, almost literally, back at the mooring. The group part ways as Ray and the Beast are staying elsewhere, but as soon as Rachel is back at the boats she texts them.

Selina and Adelaide have been under siege all day with boys throwing rocks and untying the mooring lines. Now it's Saturday night, and Cis and Rachel have listened to a man standing just outside the boat talking on the phone about how to steal the solar panels from the boats.

And another man drunkenly shouts obscene comments at a teenage girl walking alone along the tow path.

The Beast sleeps uneasily. Cis and Rachel call the police and move the boats to the side of the canal away from the tow path. Helen, their cat, is furious that her night wanderings have been interrupted.

But the mooring, situated in a recently redeveloped part of Burnley, and book-ended by two bridges, reveals itself to be the perfect trap...

The effect this will have on the project remains to be seen.

It is part of Idle Women's purpose to take up space as an act of protest...

...but they have to consider the well-being and safety of the artists who will be calling Selina their home over the coming months.

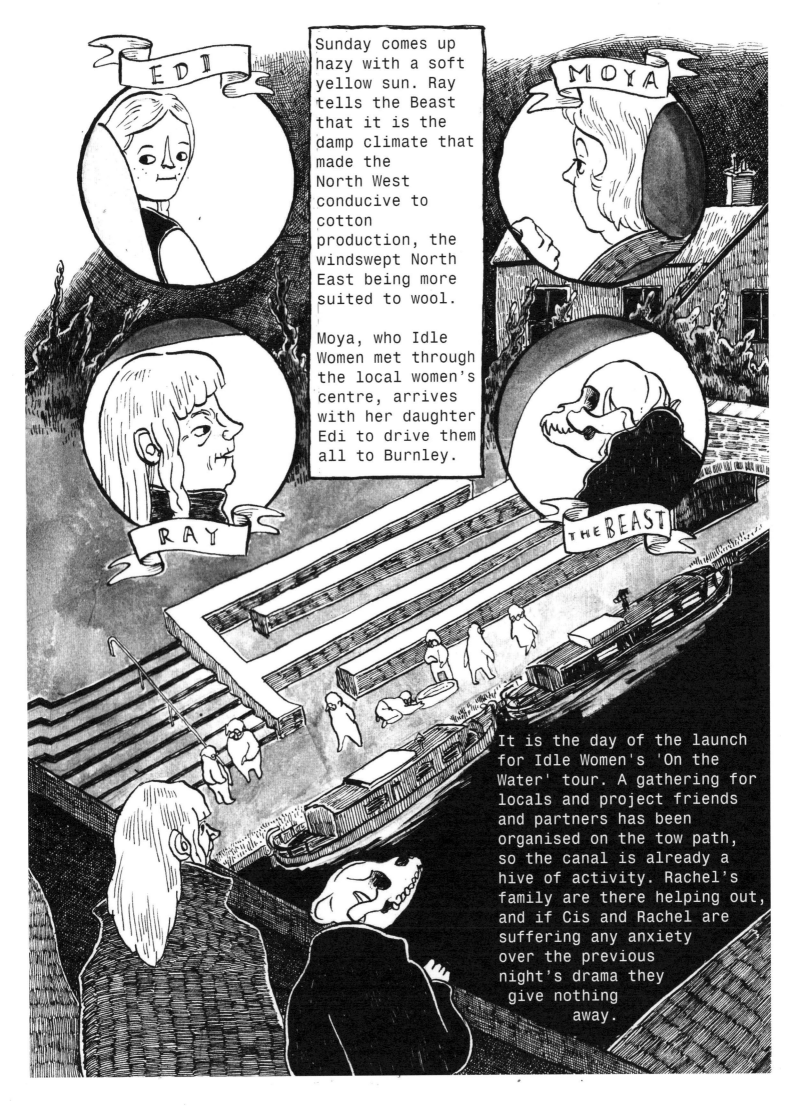

Sunday comes up hazy with a soft yellow sun. Ray tells the Beast that it is the damp climate that made the North West conducive to cotton production, the windswept North East being more suited to wool.

Moya, who Idle Women met through the local women's centre, arrives with her daughter Edi to drive them all to Burnley.

It is the day of the launch for Idle Women's 'On the Water' tour. A gathering for locals and project friends and partners has been organised on the tow path, so the canal is already a hive of activity. Rachel's family are there helping out, and if Cis and Rachel are suffering any anxiety over the previous night's drama they give nothing away.

SUNDAY OR HOW TO MAKE A SEED BOMB

The Beast is put in charge of the Seed Bomb stall.

Of all those who stop by the Beast's table, as she pretends to know how to make Seed Bombs, these three girls are her favourites.

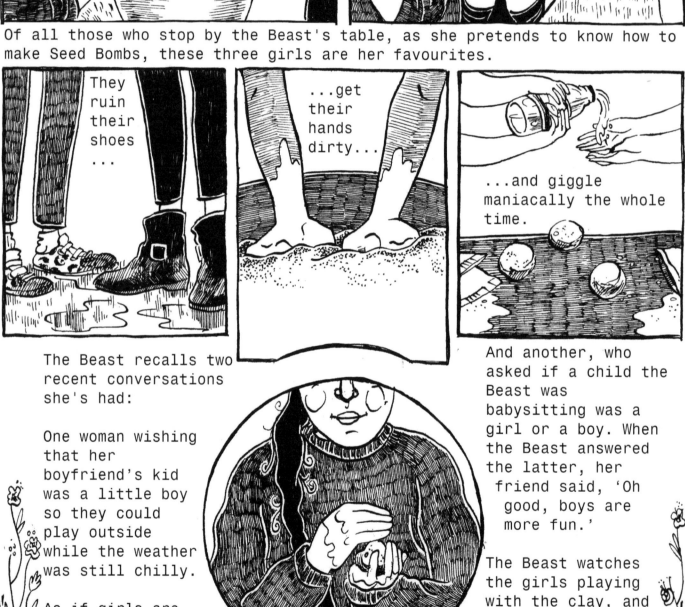

They ruin their shoes ...

...get their hands dirty...

...and giggle maniacally the whole time.

The Beast recalls two recent conversations she's had:

One woman wishing that her boyfriend's kid was a little boy so they could play outside while the weather was still chilly.

As if girls are unable to play when it's cold.

And another, who asked if a child the Beast was babysitting was a girl or a boy. When the Beast answered the latter, her friend said, 'Oh good, boys are more fun.'

The Beast watches the girls playing with the clay, and despairs at these persistent fallacies.

MOJISOLA

From her Seed Bomb stall, the Beast spots Mojisola Adebayo, a future Selina resident.

Moj moves through the crowd, willow-tall and canal water calm.

But when Moj speaks nothing is still. Her words surge and a floodgate opens; planets, stars and spiderweb nebulae spill forth. Mouths fall open in response.

Our echoes run into the canal and Adelaide and Selina receive this blessing, smiling.

You can feel it, you know, when a boat smiles.

Finally, the launch is over! Selina Cooper is officially on the water. Everyone is slightly hungover from anxious excitement.

We gather in Adelaide, drink tea, eat sugar, and lavish attention on Helen the cat.

Wrapped in blankets and well-fed, in the belly of the boat.

And as the Beast lies down, she wonders if the water is over her head.

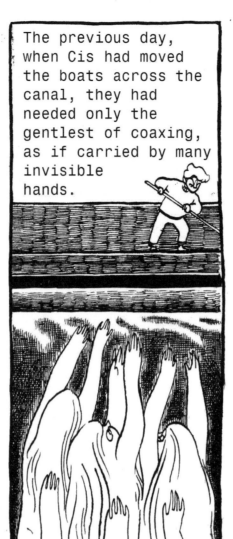

The previous day, when Cis had moved the boats across the canal, they had needed only the gentlest of coaxing, as if carried by many invisible hands.

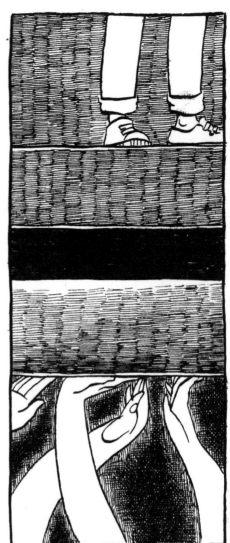

The day the Beast needs to catch her train home, however...

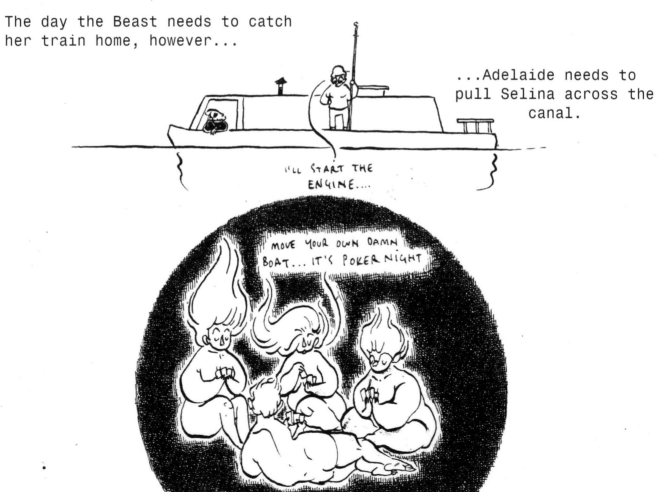

...Adelaide needs to pull Selina across the canal.

Summer 2016

CHURCH, LANCASHIRE

When the Beast returns to Lancashire that Summer, a restless hate-riddled undertow permeates everything. The EU referendum is fast approaching, and we bark at one another across a binary divide.

In Yorkshire, Labour MP Jo Cox is murdered in broad daylight.

Her killer gives his name as 'Britain First, Death to Traitors.'

When 49 people are killed in a mass shooting at a gay nightclub in Florida, it is not reported as the hate crime it is, but as a 'terrorist attack' by a non-white Muslim perpetrator. The white male Nationalist who killed Jo Cox, on the other hand, is not a terrorist, only 'mentally ill'.

GOODBYE ROSE GROVE

The Beast arrives at Rose Grove. A once sprawling railway depot at the height of the Industrial Revolution, it now has the feel of a remote atoll.

After the trouble at Burnley, Rose Grove became home to Idle Women and their first artist resident Martina Mullaney, her daughter and their dog. Now that the Spring residency is over, the boats must be moved to their Summer home. The new artist, playwright Mojisola Adebayo, arrives with her girlfriend Nicole, and as Idle Women prepare to leave, a storm begins to move in.

Canal boats are slow, their roads secret. The Beast has the feeling that they've slipped into another dimension.

Everyone takes turns driving and steering as Adelaide tows Selina through the narrow waterways.

The first crisis occurs when the wooden spoon holding the tow rope snaps!

THE WOODEN SPOON OF DISAPPOINTMENT

IS SUCCEEDED BY THE POKER OF ADEQUATE REPLACEMENT

Moj saves the day!

And then it starts to rain...

The Beast marvels at how the view from the boat transforms concrete overpasses into Ballardian cathedrals.

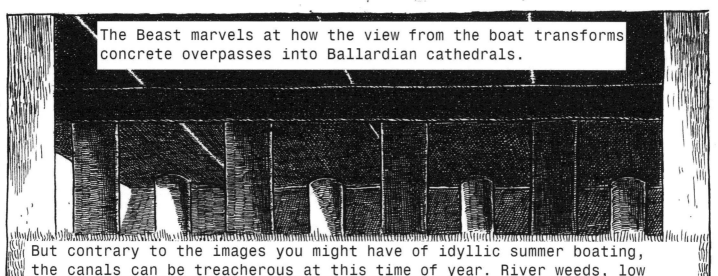

But contrary to the images you might have of idyllic summer boating, the canals can be treacherous at this time of year. River weeds, low water levels, and human detritus play havoc with Adelaide's motor.

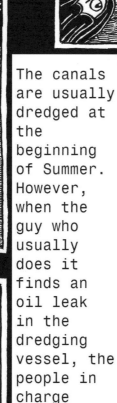

The canals are usually dredged at the beginning of Summer. However, when the guy who usually does it finds an oil leak in the dredging vessel, the people in charge wouldn't pay to have it fixed.

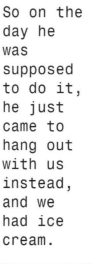

So on the day he was supposed to do it, he just came to hang out with us instead, and we had ice cream.

The weather continues to roll in, foul-tempered and wet-mouthed. The waterway crosses increasingly open countryside, and an unforgiving wind barrels over the hills and into the boats, slowing them down and starting to drive them backwards. Finally, when they are literally dragging Selina and Adelaide along with rain-soaked and rope-burned paws, someone suggests they quit for the day. Rachel soberly responds:

When darkness falls the going gets easier. Cis and Rachel take control of the boats, ushering Nicole, Moj and the Beast onto Selina to light the stove and put the kettle on.

The canal winds through a more tame, urban setting, and fenced back yards and street lights replace the wild eyes of the open countryside.

In the gloaming, Cis and Rachel bring everyone safely to Clayton-le-Moors. It's not quite the end of the road, but it's enough for today.

The Beast thinks they would have crossed many ghosts out there today; the women and children for whom this would have been a way of life.

Their labour was often unpaid and invisible. As it was on land, in the factories and in the home; so it was on water.

The early morning idyll...

... is broken by the sound of...

...jingling shackles.

41

The day holds barely a memory of yesterday's stormy weather.

The Beast meets the boats at a swing bridge and the remainder of the journey is easy. The canal has forgiven us.

We arrive at the new mooring and see a circle of horses standing over a prostrate foal. We fear it's a funeral.

THERE ARE FEW SHAPES MORE PERFECT THAN THAT OF A BABY HORSE.

There's ceremonial stamping and the little horse begins to get up. Only when it stands do the horses disband.

The new mooring at Church and Oswaldtwistle is disarmingly beautiful. Everything decaying and sad that Idle Women left behind in Rose Grove becomes fecund and hopeful here.

Michelle Wren, an artist from St. Helens and friend of Idle Women, pays a visit on that first day, engaging passing strangers and bringing fresh energy to the boats and their weary keepers.

Local teenagers Chloe and April also pass by for the first time. They will come to be a big part of this idle Summer.

The following day, Idle Women are preparing for the evening's festivities.
It is the Summer Solstice and Ramadan. The boats are going to host Iftar,
the breaking of the fast, at sundown.

Chloe and April take
Michelle on a tour of the
local horses.

And the girls remind the
Beast of the mono-cultures
that tend to proliferate in
small towns.

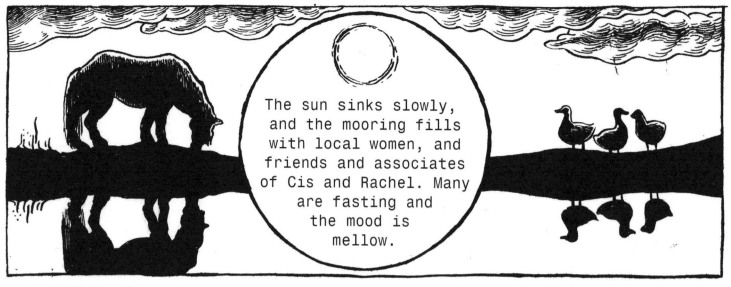

The sun sinks slowly, and the mooring fills with local women, and friends and associates of Cis and Rachel. Many are fasting and the mood is mellow.

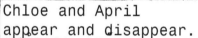

Chloe and April appear and disappear.

Michelle talks shop with some colleagues.

Nicole converses softly in Urdu.

Khushi from Fair for All wakes from a blanket nap to tell the story of her marriage: arriving home from school one day she is confronted by her father and a stern stranger.

The stranger takes Khushi to England, and while she talks positively about the financial boon the marriage has been, she has encouraged her children to choose their own partners.

The bond Khushi has with her female friends is as strong...

DO YOU REMEMBER WHEN YOU WROTE TO RIAZ...

AND I SAID I WISHED I WAS PART OF YOUR FAMILY...

AND I REPLIED "YOU ARE."

...as some of the stories they share are dark.

The damp air splits the westering sun into a rainbow and a happy fire chuckles in the gathering dusk. The Beast recognises many of the women from the Mill Hill conference. Idle Women's connections here are strengthening.

One of them is Riaz.

She reads a poem...

...conjuring Autumn.

I WROTE THAT IN THE ASDA CAR PARK WAITING FOR RIFFAT...

She smiles, slyly.

Despite one woman's enthusiastic attempt to lead everyone in a vigorous sing-a-long, many are hesitant to join in, and those observing Ramadan are happy to simply be in the space together.

Moj intuits both these energies into a call and response song that is at once inclusive without demanding too much physicality. It is the perfect way to usher in the night. The day's fasting is done. Iftar can begin.

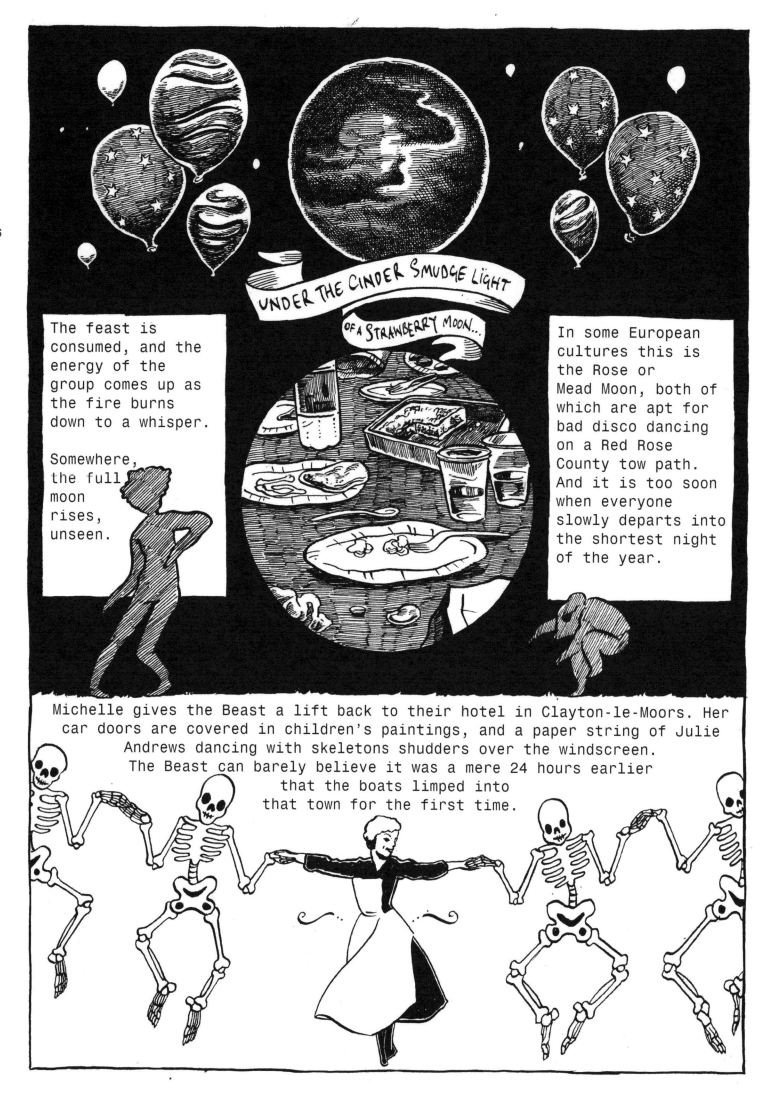

UNDER THE CINDER SMUDGE LIGHT OF A STRAWBERRY MOON...

The feast is consumed, and the energy of the group comes up as the fire burns down to a whisper.

Somewhere, the full moon rises, unseen.

In some European cultures this is the Rose or Mead Moon, both of which are apt for bad disco dancing on a Red Rose County tow path. And it is too soon when everyone slowly departs into the shortest night of the year.

Michelle gives the Beast a lift back to their hotel in Clayton-le-Moors. Her car doors are covered in children's paintings, and a paper string of Julie Andrews dancing with skeletons shudders over the windscreen. The Beast can barely believe it was a mere 24 hours earlier that the boats limped into that town for the first time.

EPILOGUE

On the last morning of the trip, the Beast and Michelle go in search of Chloe and April's 'waterfall'.

The refugee crisis and impending EU referendum permeate their conversation.

They talk of borders, racism and insidious colonial practices still rife in the U.K.

There are armed men in a field and though only hunting, their presence is unnerving.

A gun dog in training, like a bad omen, swims through the long grass looking for death.

The swimming hole looks like it's straight out of a '70s Public Information film, but the Beast recognises it as somewhere she too would have hung out as a kid.

The women turn to go, and as they walk back the Beast thinks that if kids had safe and nurturing places to be, maybe they wouldn't have to risk crumbling walls.

Or deep water.

EID AL-FITR AND BEYOND

This is first time the Beast has had to find the mooring by herself. She makes notes of the directions from the station.

Glimpsing a flash of colour from the window, she realises she can even see the boats from the train.

It's going to be so easy!

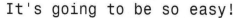

The Beast gets lost...

...finally arriving just in time to say goodbye to all the women leaving the boat.

Idle Women have begun their Summer programme with one of their weekly 'Socials'. The boats become beacons and everyone is invited to an informal gathering where Idle Women try to build bonds.

3 STORIES TOLD Me...

As the first of the the women arrive, alcohol begins to flow, and so does Lancashire's rain. One of the women thought she brought a tent, but it's only a fishing shelter. No ground sheet. No door. They fall asleep regardless, laughing at their mistake.

At the first Social, things don't quite go to plan. Women from the local women's centre come down and begin drinking as if it's a Friday night at the pub. The vodka flows, as does the rain, and a couple of them produce a tent. Only it's not a proper tent. They pass out, exposed to the elements.

At the first Social, boundaries are severely tested. The women get very drunk and one, who had no intention of going home, produces a tent. Her friend, who has recently got her life together and has a job interview in the morning, is drawn into the other's dark undertow.

The woman doesn't make it to her interview. Two women have slept outside in the rain. It is a lesson in how to maintain the boundary between being a supportive and open place, and enabling destructive behaviour. It is a tough lesson learned.

The Eid celebration is hosted in tandem with the women of Humraaz, a shelter for Black and Minority Ethnic women based in Blackburn. When everyone else has left, one of the women stays behind. Rachel and Cis have known her for six months now and her oldest child, a rambunctious 4-year old, follows Cis around like a little shadow.

The woman fled an abusive relationship and is now applying for asylum in the U.K. She narrowly avoided being put into a detention centre while her claim was processed. There are many single mothers who are not so lucky.

The woman slips out of view when two of the local police officers show up. They are friendly with Idle Women and are stopping by to say hello. The sight of the uniforms understandably make the woman nervous, even though she's done nothing wrong.

When asked about their relationship with the local police, Rachel says...

..." it's complicated."

Karen Mirza, a future artist in residence on the Selina Cooper, is also spending the day at the boats. She folds away the paper decorations that had adorned the tow path, carefully restoring them to their original state as if undoing a complicated spell. While occupied with this task, she talks about mediums and psychic phenomena. She tells the Beast about Helen Duncan; famous for producing ectoplasm while interacting with the psychic plane, and infamous for being the last woman imprisoned under the Witchcraft Act of 1753, for revealing war secrets during a seance in 1944.

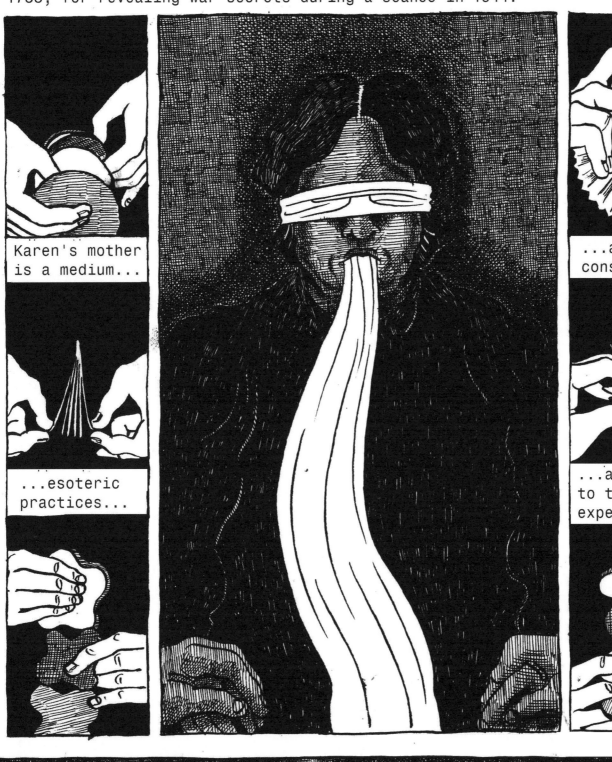

Karen's mother is a medium...

...esoteric practices...

...and she considers...

...as integral to the human experience.

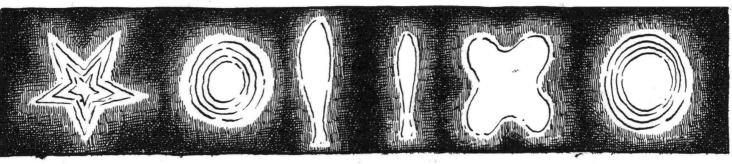

That evening, Karen and Moj take the Beast to a boxing class at the Kokoro Gym in Accrington.

TALK TO ME DARLING. TALK TO ME DARLING.

8-year old boys who have learned to mimic the older men catcall them on the street corner

The class is led by Alison Curtis, the first female boxing coach to earn a professional licence in the U.K. The Beast has never boxed before, and the lesson is difficult, exhilarating and fun. Afterwards, Moj asks Alison if she might bring some of the women from Humraaz along. Many of them have experienced intimate partner violence, and self-defence sessions may empower them.

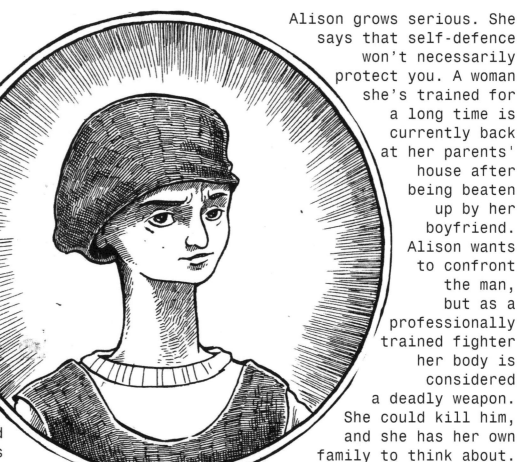

Alison grows serious. She says that self-defence won't necessarily protect you. A woman she's trained for a long time is currently back at her parents' house after being beaten up by her boyfriend. Alison wants to confront the man, but as a professionally trained fighter her body is considered a deadly weapon. She could kill him, and she has her own family to think about.

52

Karen, Moj and the Beast have either known someone close to them, or have experienced living in an abusive situation. They know how helpless and frustrating it feels to be the one sitting in the car with the engine running, waiting for someone they love to be ready to take that first risk and leave. Many of the women at Humraaz have shared their stories of escape and rescue...

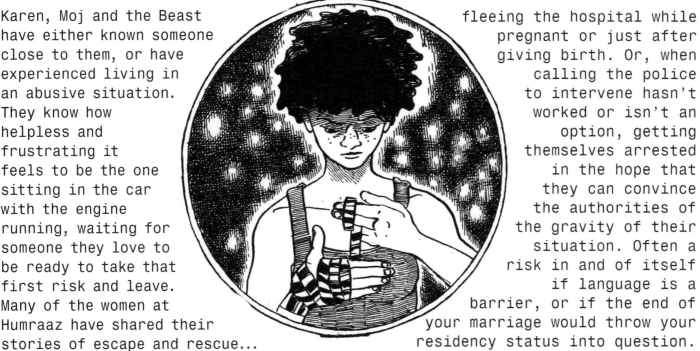

fleeing the hospital while pregnant or just after giving birth. Or, when calling the police to intervene hasn't worked or isn't an option, getting themselves arrested in the hope that they can convince the authorities of the gravity of their situation. Often a risk in and of itself if language is a barrier, or if the end of your marriage would throw your residency status into question.

53

When Moj, Karen and the Beast eventually arrive back at the boats with that night's dinner, they find Cis and Rachel waiting outside Adelaide. The Beast has the keys.

Moj and Karen talk about being mixed race. Karen, whose father is Pakistani and mother Irish. Moj's father is Nigerian and her mother Dutch.

The artists talk about how their heritage has shaped and betrayed them. Not only fighting racism and implicit biases, but also how these identities have shaped their work.

A DETOUR FROM BREAKFAST TO PRESTON

54

At breakfast the next day a woman named Susannah joins the Beast at her table. Susannah is in town to view a house, as she's been living with her sister since her own home was destroyed in last year's floods. She tells her story over tea and toast.

The woman's life has been a colourful patchwork of entrepreneurship and lovers ever since her husband died in 1999. A second woman joins them. She luxuriates at a hotel when visiting her 90-year old grandma so as not to have to spend too much time with her family.

Later, with time to kill in Preston, the Beast finds the Martyrs Memorial. It stands in memory to four protestors killed by the military in 1842.

It reads: 'Remember, remember people of proud Preston, progress has not been achieved without great sacrifice.'

The thought briefly shadows her mind, 'But who is being sacrificed? And for whose progress?' Then it is time to get her train.

Since they showed up on that very first day, the teenagers Chloe and April have been returning to the boats regularly for workshops with Moj. The Beast joins them one rainy Friday afternoon. Moj starts with a portraiture exercise, where they draw one another's face without breaking eye contact or looking at the lines they're making. It's intense.

THE BEAST by CHLOE

MOJ by APRIL

APRIL by MOJ

After this warm up, Moj and the girls return to what they've been working on for the last few weeks: an 'Alphabet of Women's Pleasure'.

The girls work on more drawings, and later add a verse to their alphabet poem that celebrates the joys of riding horses to Blackpool for ice cream.

While horses feature heavily in the girls' imaginations, the animals themselves, just a stone's throw across the canal, are off limits.

The owner had asked for the girls' numbers so they could arrange times to come and feed the horses.

It later transpired that he had been sending them 'inappropriate' texts.

So often, sources of pleasure are corrupted into sources of shame.

That night, Moj is talking on a panel as part of Kinara Festival, a celebration of Islamic culture held in venues across Pennine Lancashire.

Where was that play?

At the tea shop, remember?

Events are only running on weekends, that audience members Riz and Aisha have found difficult, as that's when they work.

Tonight the panel

discuss how faith

influences their art.

Peter Sanderson is a photographer.

Moj talks about Muhammad Ali.

Actor Asif Khan is in the play 'Love, Bombs and Apples'.

He talks about his conversion to Islam

And her work in Palestine and teenage evangelism.

He often finds he is the one 'Muslim friend.'

Afterwards, Idle Women head to Shandar's, one of their favourite Blackburn haunts, and talk about the night. The Beast observes that Peter, a white convert to Islam, was quick to criticise elements of the religion, while Asif, whose social circle was predominantly white drama school students, constantly had to defend it. It doesn't escape anyone's attention that whilst the audience was predominantly South Asian women, there was no female Muslim voice on stage.

Idle Women drive out to hike part of the Pendle Way.

These hikes have been a monthly occurence, paired with a book group reading of Silvia Federici's 'Caliban and the Witch.'

Rachel and Cis wanted to include the hikes in the Pendle Walking Festival programme.

For a while, Cis and Rachel have been accompanying an asylum seeker from Humraaz to the supermarket.

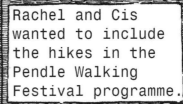

But the man in charge took issue with it being for women only.

It's difficult for her with two small children, no car, and no cash for buses or taxis.

Despite one of Idle Women's partners fighting for them...

And while she still has to use the government issue Aspen card to access her funds, it helps to have middle class white people fight your corner if the cashier makes a fuss.

...ultimately they are denied.

The Pendle Way is 45 miles of Lancashire's shaggy coat landscape, with picturesque villages and industrial scars. It also capitalises on the witch trials that took place here in the 1600s. This is the reason Idle Women are walking it whilst reading Silvia Federici's book. It examines the subjugation of the peasant body (represented by the labourers of the North), and the crushing oppression of women (fashioned into witches), which occured during the accumulation period of Western capitalism.

58

While they walk, Rachel and Cis teach the Beast all about plants.

HAWTHORN

If you are a pagan, bringing blossoming hawthorn into your house in May brings good luck. If you are Christian, it will kill your mother.

FOXGLOVE

Foxglove (or Digitalis) can be used as heart medicine, but it is difficult to dose accurately, so people just call it poison.

Reading Federici, and listening to Rachel talk about the 'Blood Moon Gossip' at the event at Khushi's factory, has completely altered the idea of witches in the Beast's mind. Although she had known the witch trials were a travesty, because the symbol of the witch has been so successfully co-opted into monster and myth, she hadn't properly considered the hunting and killing of witches as the hunting and killing of women.

The three reach a bilberry field and take it as a sign that it is time for lunch.

BILBERRIES

The last time Cis bought bilberries at a market she was told they were imported from Poland because British farmers couldn't find pickers for the crop.

MEADOWSWEET

Meadowsweet contains the ingredients for aspirin, and its heady scent heralds the end of the walk. The women must return to the real world.

ONE OF THOSE WHIRL-WIND GOODBYES

60

Idle Women have been given permission to paint a mural on the side of the old factory at the mooring, so the Beast makes one final trip to Church to help finish the painting.

She arrives in one of the soft Summer downpours that have become synonymous with the place.

Over decaf coffee (it was all there was), Rachel talks about how Moj's residency has exceeded all their expectations. Selina has become a creative and healing space for a diverse group of women and girls. Leaving here is going to be hard on everyone.

Over the course of a summer...

...friends have been made...

...walls broken down...

...and new bonds forged.

The rain continues. Moj hosts a writing workshop on board Selina and women sit around reading, writing and simply taking up space together. The Beast can feel it is a powerful thing.

Sunday forgives them, and although the clouds roll wildly across the morning sky, it is dry enough for painting. The artist Raksha Patel has been brought in to design the mural and co-ordinate the work. The Beast meets her along the tow path and they walk to the boats, Raksha telling the now familiar story of an artist who has lived in London for most of her professional career, watching in horror as it aggressively morphs into one big, unaffordable, homogenous office block.

The mural draws on the 'Alphabet of Women's Pleasure', the poem Moj wrote with 80 women during the Summer. Phrases based on the poem are woven into the natural beauty of the Lancashire countryside. Words in English and Urdu flower in the undergrowth and shape-shift into geese.

The Beast meets Natalie for the first time. A woman who trained as an artist, but hasn't practised recently, because life has ways of changing your plans. Under the gentle guidance of Raksha, she flourishes here.

And then it is time to go...

The Beast runs for another train. The work goes on behind her.

Every artist who lives on Selina finds a way to make her home. For the Beast, Moj's residency will always be defined by the large framed picture of Mae Jemison, the first Black woman in space, which took pride of place on the wall. Not only is she culturally and historically significant, but the smile Jemison wears as she floats in zero gravity is one of pure pleasure.

And that's what it felt like we were that Summer; celestial bodies floating in the water and taking up space. And it was beautiful.

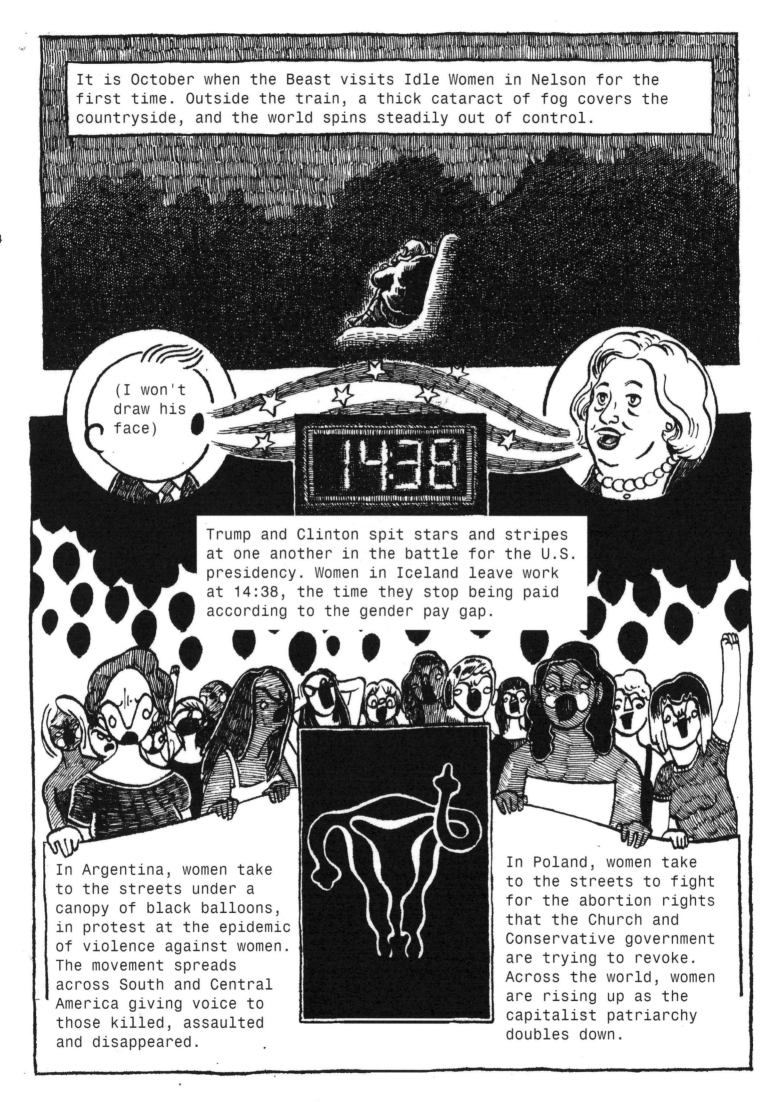

It is October when the Beast visits Idle Women in Nelson for the first time. Outside the train, a thick cataract of fog covers the countryside, and the world spins steadily out of control.

64

(I won't draw his face)

Trump and Clinton spit stars and stripes at one another in the battle for the U.S. presidency. Women in Iceland leave work at 14:38, the time they stop being paid according to the gender pay gap.

In Argentina, women take to the streets under a canopy of black balloons, in protest at the epidemic of violence against women. The movement spreads across South and Central America giving voice to those killed, assaulted and disappeared.

In Poland, women take to the streets to fight for the abortion rights that the Church and Conservative government are trying to revoke. Across the world, women are rising up as the capitalist patriarchy doubles down.

The Nelson mooring is a strange combination of Church and Rose Grove. All the romantic beauty of the former, behind the black iron smile of the latter.

65

Rachel is clearing Autumnal detritus from Selina's deck. Between the smell of damp leaves and the woodsmoke, it has never felt further from the Summer.

They go inside where a fire is burning and the kettle is on. "It's been hard to reach the women here", Rachel says. She and Cis feel very exposed and vulnerable in Nelson as lesbian women.

ARE YOU MARRIED?

YES.

GO BACK TO YOUR HUSBAND THEN.

It's half term, so there are children playing in the warren-like streets near the boats. Rachel and Cis come up with a plan to engage them while maintaining good boundaries.

The women leave little assignments for the kids. The key for the postbox has been entrusted to one of the local girls, empowering them without excluding the boys.

CAN WE BRING YOU OUR WORLDS?

(AND THEN THERE IS THE PERSISTENT FEELING...)

WHY AM I LAYING AN EXTRA PLACE AT THE TABLE?

(...AN UNSETTLING SENSE...)

AM I FORGETTING SOMEONE?

(...THAT THE WHOLE DAMN PLACE IS HAUNTED.)

FEELS LIKE SOMEONE JUST LEFT THE ROOM.

The unseen women, the undertow of male violence, and this niggling unease has given Nelson an unsettling, haunted quality. The Beast and Rachel talk about imagination being akin to intuition.

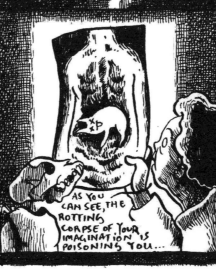

AS YOU CAN SEE, THE ROTTING CORPSE OF YOUR IMAGINATION IS POISONING YOU...

The Beast thinks the human imagination is often criminally undervalued. She pictures it as a major organ in the body that will sicken and die without proper care and attention.

To lighten the mood, the Beast mentions how excited she is to see Moj. It is the opening night of her play 'Muhammad Ali and Me', which is set to be performed in several local gyms. "Oh", Rachel says, ominously. "You haven't heard..."

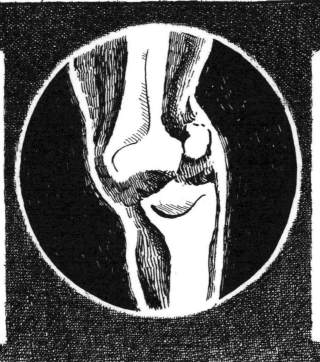

During a performance of the play in London earlier that week, an errant step had given way and Moj had injured her knee. She finished the show before going to the emergency room where the dislocation was misdiagnosed.

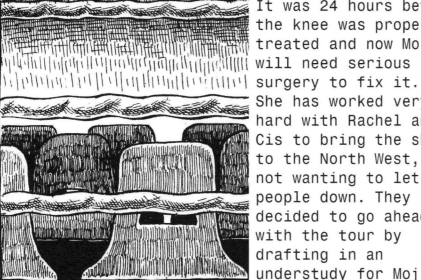

It was 24 hours before the knee was properly treated and now Moj will need serious surgery to fix it. She has worked very hard with Rachel and Cis to bring the show to the North West, not wanting to let people down. They decided to go ahead with the tour by drafting in an understudy for Moj.

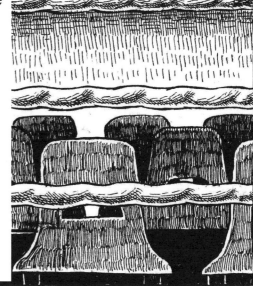

The first show is at Kokoro, the Accrington gym Moj attended during her residency. Natalie of the mural painting, collects tickets.

In the front row is the boxing trainer Alison's husband Justin with their daughter, who convinced him to put the show on.

Everyone is nervous, but the gym begins to get busy. Several friends of Idle Women have come, some from as far as Manchester.

Crin the Technician

Alison the Producer

Muhammad Ali had died the previous summer. The Beast recalls Moj telling her how much she had cried and the depth of her grief when she heard the news. However, the Beast hadn't fully appreciated the significance of the boxer to Moj until she saw the play. A semi-autobiographical story of a girl who falls through the cracks in the care system, and how Muhammad Ali helps her to survive and process her trauma. The writing is so strong that even with scripts in hand, the three performances make the blood in the Beast's ears roar.

Sheron Wray

Deni, Moj's understudy clearly has an intimate and loving knowledge of the script. Charlie slips between characters with such deftness that one is left unsure as to whether they're the same actor. Jackie seamlessly integrates British Sign Language into the play through her energetic performance as the umpire.

The show is enthusiastically received, even with its challenging subject matter. A kid wearing a Muhammad Ali t-shirt gets his photo taken with the cast at the end. In the short Q&A that follows, director Sheron Wray makes a brief statement about the London production. The Beast only knows that the play has retained its power, and then some.

The fact that in the current climate of austerity 'Muhammad Ali and Me' can be staged at all is a small miracle. Lancashire is being devastated by cuts. Art spaces, libraries and essential services are going dark all over the county.

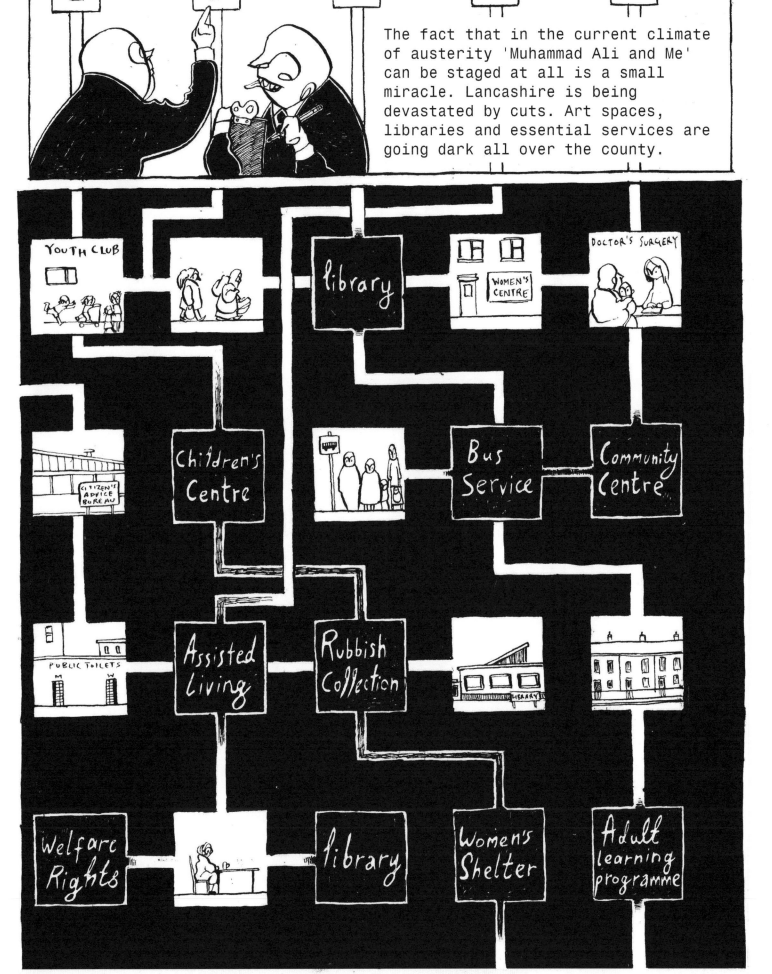

The tour of 'Muhammad Ali and Me' is a resounding success. Most of the performances have been well attended thanks to both community involvement and the local relationships Idle Women have forged. The final show, as part of Burnley Literature Festival is no exception.

It is so popular that the regular seating is soon filled up. People perch on the woodsmoke-infused camping chairs borrowed from the boats, and children drape themselves over unused exercise equipment. Luca, Deni and Crin's son, sits amid a forest of chair legs, colouring book forgotten, rapt by his mother's performance

The Q&A after the show is as easy as a chat with old friends. There are several D/deaf audience members who discuss Jackie's role with her and the importance of the integration of British Sign Language.

(Mandatory post-show tag in the boxing ring.)

The Beast also notes that when Deni as Muhammad Ali, talks about his conversion to Islam as a rejection of white America's brutal racism, it feels subversive in the current climate of Islamophobia and the Black Lives Matter movement.

It is nearly Halloween, so after the show Rachel and the Beast return to the boats laden with firewood and gourds for carving.

The Beast has also felt an absence, but her ghost has been Cis. When they arrive she is sitting alone and still, in the gathering dusk.

Halloween, or Samhain (Sa-ween) if you want to get pagan about it, is the pre-Christian New Year, the time when the veil between this world and the next is thought to be at its thinnest.

Those who observed Samhain believed that Winter, despite its snow covered silence, was chaos as people went into the season not knowing if they would survive it.

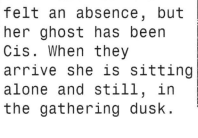

Carving little demon faces into root vegetables, and leaving them around your homestead tricked the bad spirits who were wont to wander at this time of year, into believing you were already cursed. Being respectful of one another's territory, the demons would leave people ever so slightly more likely to make it to Spring. That night Rachel, Cis and the Beast carve about twenty.

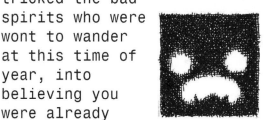

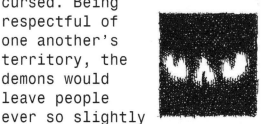

Because the last thing Idle Women need this Autumn is a malevolent spirit making trouble at the mooring.

The next day, the Beast finally gets to spend some time with resident artist Karen Mirza. She too, has found engaging with the local women difficult. There was one successful session where the women brought their children, but it has not been repeated.

Over coffee, Karen tells the Beast about some boys who have been coming to smoke by the mooring. They were calling the women only space sexist and she defended it by highlighting the different spaces men and women are given for worship at mosque.

Karen goes on to talk about her complicated relationship with her own faith.

Her father is a Hyderabadi Muslim, but she finds his conservative religious practice restricting. She has recently spent a lot of time in Turkey, and is drawn to their cultural approach to the religion. She also has a deep affinity with the esoteric practices of her Irish mother, which would be considered blasphemy within strict interpretations of most religions.

Sache & Sugar

Karen and the Beast walk the canal to...

jarmara

the Witch Museum in Barrowford. Like many places

Vinegar

it struggles to reconcile the tourism aspect

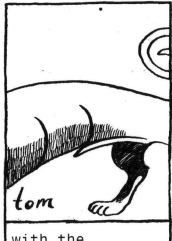

tom

with the persecution and killing of women.

As a refreshing surprise however, they meet Bob at the Pendle Heritage Centre who talks excitedly about how a research student recently introduced him to the idea of the witch trials as gendercide. The Beast hopes he has incorporated this into the tour.

BOB

But, as Karen and the Beast explore the exhibition, there is no evidence of anything so progressive. Some dry historical context is given to the local witch trials, but there is little criticism or attempt at dismantling the supernatural trappings of the story.

At the end of the exhibition there is a short film which concludes that, thanks to the Enlightenment, witches ceased to exist.

"OR DID THEY?", the film asks, as a candle is ominously extinguished. Somehow, Bob remains the most radical part of the exhibition.

The Beast can understand Pendle Heritage Centre playing it safe though. It's an independent entity, which has fought hard to preserve its buildings and cultural significance.

On the Beast's walk home a large witch effigy stands in the garden of a terraced house, pointing menacingly at the street. (Women will be difficult monsters to rid ourselves of.)

The trials of the Pendle witches are some of the most infamous in English history. From accusation to execution, they took place from March to August of 1612. The story begins one fine Spring morning, when a pedlar meets Alizon Device on the road. She asks him if he'll sell her some pins.

The pedlar refuses, (very rude).

And moments later, suffers what was probably a stroke.

But this is the 1600s, so he accuses her of witchcraft.

Initially, this leads to the arrest of Alizon Device, her grandmother Elizabeth Southerns, alias Old Demdike and another two women, Anne Whittle also known as Chattox, and her daughter Anne Redfern. However, when friends and family gather at the Device family home to discuss what can be done for the women, rumours spread that the meeting was a witch's sabbat and eight more people are arrested.

It is 9-year old Jennet Device who will be coerced into condemning them all, and while Old Demdike will die in prison and one of the accused will be acquitted, ten people will hang. As an adult, Jennet too will be tried for witchcraft and put to death.

THE WITCH KING.

One of the reasons witch trials proliferated in this era was due to King James I's obsession with the phenomena after witnessing similar witch hysteria in Denmark. His paranoia was probably exacerbated by the Bye and Gunpowder plots that marked his early reign.

Convinced it is a witch's curse that nearly scuppers the ship taking him back to Scotland, the king famously held his first trials in North Berwick, and went on to write The Daemonologie, a kind of witchfinder handbook.

The demonisation and persecution of women under the auspices of witchcraft increased as the rise of capitalist systems disenfranchised and oppressed them.

Whilst James I's interest in witches declined dramatically in his later years, the witch trials would not only plague England throughout the 17th and 18th centuries, but also be exported to the New World.

HUBBLE BUBBLE TOIL AND CURSES.

Macbeth was written during the reign of James I, and the Wyrd Sisters are apparently modelled on details from his Daemonologie.

The supernatural witch has persisted, while the reality of women being tried and killed has been erased.

Even the term 'witch hunt' has become a general term for persecution in the global West...

WITCHES WERE WISE WOMEN   MIDWIVES AND NURSES

In 1753, the law was revised. A witch could no longer perform supernatural acts, but if she could cure an ailment, divine your future or perform an abortion, she could be fined or imprisoned as a witch. England moved from burning heretics to controlling the means by which one could earn a living. Some people have noticed this pattern being repeated in other places around the world, often post-colonially, and in newly burgeoning capitalist systems.

SAMHAIN

On Samhain proper there are candles lit for the dead...

...and wine mulled for the living.

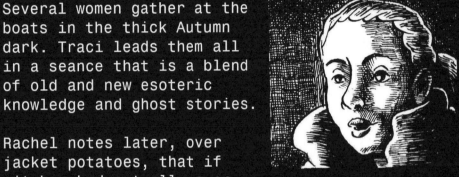

Several women gather at the boats in the thick Autumn dark. Traci leads them all in a seance that is a blend of old and new esoteric knowledge and ghost stories.

Rachel notes later, over jacket potatoes, that if witches had actually ever had magical powers they never would have been caught.

But there was a time perhaps, when we were better at trusting our intuition, and more aligned with nature than we are today.

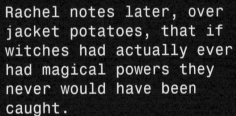

SYMPATHY FOR THE DEVIL...

And like a shadow given life in this wicked season, Helen stalks between the glowing, grinning gourds. She has been leaving little murders all over the boat. Canal life in the North has made them all a bit more feral.

When the Beast visits Nelson she stays at a hotel in Brierfield.

The interior is a logic-defying warren of corridors and staircases.

FROM BRIERFIELD

The glassy spider eyes of empty factories peer across the water.

The tow path is yellow gold for lost wealth, and brick red for lost industry.

TO

The Beast feels like the last one left alive.

Belligerent geese pick fights with everybody.

Then, the strange, visceral shock of another person.

A wonderland of discarded plastic and destruction...

BURNLEY.

...the canal sneaks up on Burnley, spitting the Beast out from under a bridge where she has sometimes caught the lightning sapphire streak of a kingfisher.

This is how the Beast passes her downtime.

78

That night is Open Boat.

A weekly event where a general call goes out to local women, and Karen hosts a themed evening on Selina.

The Beast waits on the street to guide anyone who arrives down to the boats. She watches children slip between houses like shadows, and a sickle moon hangs clear and sharp above the chimneys. Natalie, and a woman called Sue who was also at the Samhain celebration arrive, and the evening commences. The theme is cartomancy, but somehow the conversation is diverted early on to body shame and eating disorders.

THE MODEL

THE BULEMIC

THE SIZEIST

THE WEIGHTWATCHER

When Karen was 17 she had an audition with a modelling agency. They examined her like a horse; checking her teeth and gait, then told her to lose half a stone and come back in two weeks.

Karen then became obessively aware of eating, and gained a stone.

The Beast recalls someone who binges and purges like she is observing a daily ritual.

Natalie's 7-year old nephew's family have adopted a vegan diet to be 'healthy', which to them means 'thin'. The child has developed a horrible kind of Fat Phobia and now refuses to hug his aunt.

When Sue was 11, her mother sent her to Weight Watchers. Now in her mid-forties, she says it took her years to rebuild a healthy relationship to food and her body.

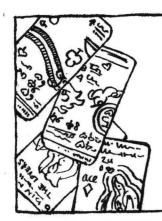

Cartomancy

Karen manages to bring the session back to her chosen theme. Cartomancy is a form of divination using regular playing cards, that rose to prominence among the working class after an import tax made Tarot cards unaffordable.

THE JACK OF CLUBS	THE ACE OF SPADES	THE 9 OF DIAMONDS	THE JOKER

	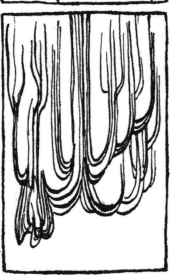	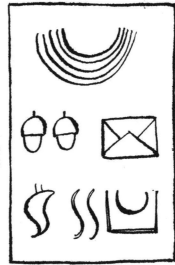	

Karen presents artist and occultist Austen Osman Spare's intricately hand-drawn deck and we all make our own cards. When Cis and Rachel arrive there is talk of developing a communal deck for Idle Women.

Then the activity dissolves into a birthday party for Rachel. There is Stollen bread and sherry, and tea for those who don't drink. The conversation meanders between the heavy and the light, and the night draws in a little closer.

PAMELA·COLMAN·SMITH

During her research, the Beast comes across Pamela Colman Smith, the illustrator responsible for some of the most iconic Tarot cards in the world. Her Rider-Waite deck is synonymous with the practice, but bears only the names of the two men who designed it.

Colman Smith was a mixed race woman born in Jamaica. She moved to London and trained as an illustrator, working in the art departments of theatres, but completed the Rider-Waite commission in a tiny apartment in New York. Upon her death, she left everything to her long-time partner, Nora Lake.

On Wednesday, the Beast meets Karen in Nelson. She is early, so spends time at the public library, writing.

Libraries are important. Stop closing them.

At The Shop, a social enterprise...

...and art space that used to be a post office, teenagers...

...serve them tea, and spinach soup.

Later that month...

DAMN KEYS...

WAIT...

...WHAT?

...an eviction notice appears.

BURLINGTON GOLD

NOTICE OF REPO

The landlord seizes the property and The Shop is given one day to clear the premises.

The rent was paid, and as far as those running the space could see, the eviction was completely unwarranted.

The community rallies to empty the space before the bailiffs come. At the time of writing, it remains vacant.

THE SOCIAL

·FARA·

Idle Women have continued to hold Socials like they did in the Summer, only now they are at the Beaconsfield Family Centre. Tonight, there is Halloween crafting, and many familiar faces.

The key-holder for the space is Fara. She was a founding member of The Chai Centre, which provides health services for local Black and Minority Ethnic women.

Fara was also part of a cohort...

...who tried to defend the community...

...against the government clearances.

Rows of houses now stand empty and vandalised...

...by kids whose rage they cannot name.

If they even stand at all.

Later that night,
a thing does not
happen.

The only thing
the Beast is
allowed to record
is that it was
early November.

Her toes were
going numb in her
sneakers, and her
fingers were
nothing but
memories stolen
by the bitter
evening air.

The mist
lingered in the
valley across
from Tabor Lane
making the
distant lights
flare into
planets.

Above, the sky
remained so clear
that the stars
were as immediate
and loud as a
choir of small,
bright voices.

Three almost-
strangers stopped
and stared,
hypnotised by
this urban
poetry...

...until the
painful ache of
cold in their
bones told them
that it was time
to go home.

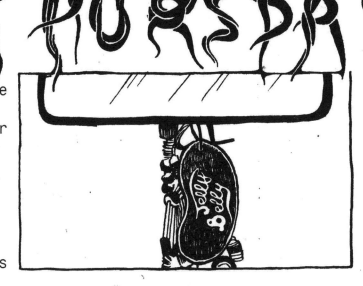

Idle Women and the Beast are driving into Blackburn for a radio interview and a Humraaz workshop. Time is tight and the day's schedule is already a nearly full Tetris screen.

We arrive and split up. The Beast and Rachel in search of the interview location, Cis in search of art supplies.

Rachel is supposed to be talking to Radio Lancashire about 'Muhammad Ali and Me.'

But with the tour finished, she decides just to promote Idle Women.

Sally Naden, who was present at Selina's launch, conducts the interview. It's nice to talk about how far they've come with someone who was there at the beginning.

The interview runs late, and by the time the trio are on the road again it is nearly midday. As with any vulnerable group, their relationship with the women of Humraaz is delicate.

Blackburn
A579 (A666)
MORE MILES THAN YOU HAVE TIME TO COVER

Humraaz are one of their most important local alliances, and Cis painfully feels their lateness.

Idle Women are meeting Humraaz at The Bureau, another newly-formed art space in an ex-public building (in this case a former Citizens Advice Bureau).

Yaz and Salma tell the Beast a little about Humraaz: it was founded in 2002 by female community activists who saw that when women in their community were victims of domestic abuse...

..on top of the psychological and financial barriers, they often lacked the language skills, or did not have recourse to public funds if their immigration status was tied to their marriage.

By providing support, life skills and community, Humraaz aims to give women the best opportunity possible for forging a life for themselves and their children beyond abusive situations.

On the periphery, Cis tries to locate a woman whose taxi driver wouldn't bring her to The Bureau. Over pizza, the women of Humraaz discuss their vision for a women only taxi service led by, and for, sisters of colour. Then there are more birthday surprises for Rachel.

The workshop begins with a little black cloth being laid out and strewn with various little objects. If she feels like it, a woman may pick an object that reminds her of a personal story. A few of them feel comfortable enough to share:

"Although it is painful to burn, it is also a source of light. It is better to burn and glow, than to be extinguished."

"Like the limestone, I too am filled with holes, but still in one piece"

"The bobbin reminds me of the textile industries that brought my parents to England."

"The crayon reminds me of a prize I won for anatomical drawing while studying medicine. My father was so proud."

"The demystification of nature has become essential to me after growing up in a city."

Finally: a woman picks up the little fossil and mimes a game of hopscotch to everyone, eliciting her childhood.

The Beast must set up a room for storytelling.

She is given access to the sacred crafts cupboard and all its glittery treasure.

A little girl keeps the Beast company. They talk drawings.

89

The session is over, but one woman waits behind. Usually Cis and Rachel take her shopping.

But today, time is against them. They encourage another woman to accompany her, and call them a taxi.

Despite the afternoon's successes, Cis can't help feeling this is a failure.

The final port of call that day is Gannow Lane, where artist Michelle Wren has been working with the locals over the last few months to try and keep their community centre open.

GANNOW LANE

She's been holding various workshops with local women and children, and this will be her last night.

The room feels like a carnival and smells of acrylic ink from the screenprinting sessions.

Karen leaves quickly in order to meet a visiting writer and activist off the train.

The greedy Beast sees food and thinks it's probably a good time for a snack.

It is a terrible time for a snack.

Cis has begun to call the growling knot of rage that has festered inside her for the last few weeks, The Black Root.

Exhausted by the work, all the anger coiled up inside her erupts in a torrent of rage and frustration.

The Beast stands slack-jawed as her brain cycles through the various options of response:

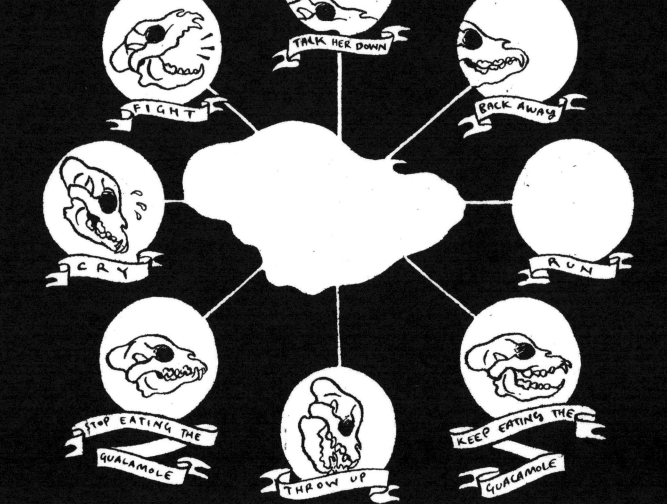

TALK HER DOWN

FIGHT

BACK AWAY

CRY

RUN

STOP EATING THE GUACAMOLE

THROW UP

KEEP EATING THE GUACAMOLE

When it's over though, in theme with the day, there is no time to deal with the aftermath.

As they're clearing the hall, Michelle realises her wallet is missing. She confronts the kids calmly, without accusation. She simply tells them that while she doesn't care too much about the purse or the money, she would like the driving licence back as it's a pain to replace.

The way Michelle talks to the kids, and the way they respond, is testament to the relationships she's built and the work she's done here.

91

After she says her piece, she takes a couple of the girls to see some of the work they made. Everyone is tired, but so generous with their love, and their grief.

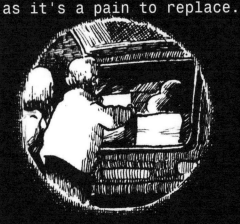  

Rachel puts the theft down to the pain of leaving, which often happens when this kind of community work ends. Despite everything they've achieved, the day doesn't end any lighter than it began.

Back at the boats, Cis and Rachel retire, exhausted.

The Beast goes to Selina to see Karen and meet Rahila Gupta for the first time.

Rahila is a writer and activist, and one of the original founders of Southall Black Sisters.

The Sisters first got together in 1978 to fight against violence in all its forms.

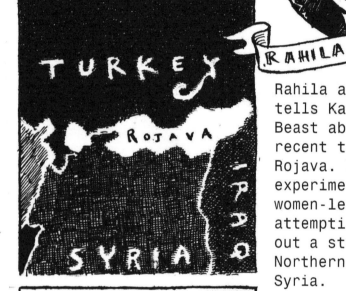

Rahila animatedly tells Karen and the Beast about her recent trip to Rojava. Rojava is an experiment in women-led revolution, attempting to carve out a state on the Northern border of Syria.

Rojava, where gender parity is not enough...

...but actively favours women.

Based on the teachings of imprisoned Turkish rebel Öcalan, the women are trying to construct a system that completely rejects patriarchal hierarchies.

There is a man and a woman in every leadership role.

And everyone, from ferryperson to government official, are paid the same.

It is a bold vision indeed, and under threat, not only ideologically, but because it has established itself on the edge of Syria's unabating civil war.

The Shifting Loyalties Conference that the Beast nearly forgets to attend is something Idle Women have been organising for months, and their last big event of the year.

The Beast finally arrives at Coldwell Activity Centre in the the deepest of midwinter darkness.

It is a weekend gathering of friends, local women, artists, intellectuals and activists. That first night, waiting for the strays to arrive, everyone settles down to watch Lizzie Borden's 'Born in Flames', set in an '80s dystopian New York where poor women of colour arm themselves for a revolution.

95

Silvia Federici, author of 'Caliban and the Witch', is present at the Conference, and critical of the film's call to arms. She argues that if women were compensated for their work, it would change how society valued their labour and in turn, women themselves.

While the Beast can understand her point...

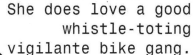

She does love a good whistle-toting vigilante bike gang.

The next morning the Conference begins in earnest.

The first women to speak are Jashmin Patel and Ikamara Larasi from Purple Drum, a feminist organisation dedicated to addressing violence against women and girls. They show examples of how pop culture and social media can perpetuate violence, but also provide a platform for positively changing narratives.

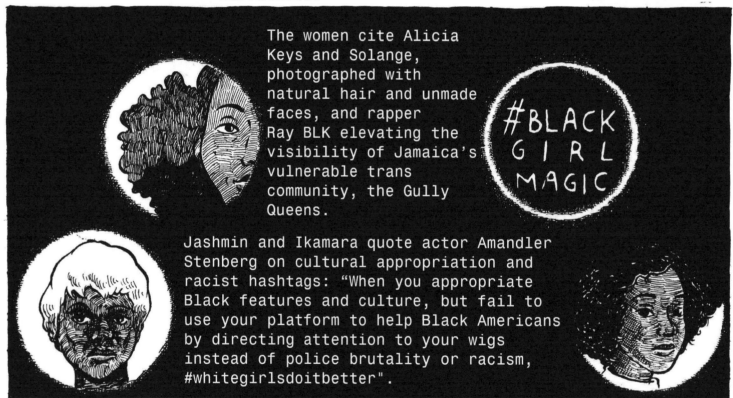

The women cite Alicia Keys and Solange, photographed with natural hair and unmade faces, and rapper Ray BLK elevating the visibility of Jamaica's vulnerable trans community, the Gully Queens.

#BLACK GIRL MAGIC

Jashmin and Ikamara quote actor Amandler Stenberg on cultural appropriation and racist hashtags: "When you appropriate Black features and culture, but fail to use your platform to help Black Americans by directing attention to your wigs instead of police brutality or racism, #whitegirlsdoitbetter".

The women conclude with a short film produced by Purple Drum, in which Black women and women of colour speak out about the micro and macro racist and sexist aggressions they have endured, often normalised on a daily basis, in order to move through the world. It is a disarmingly powerful piece.

Claire Heuchan is a Black, Scottish, lesbian feminist who writes about her experiences within these communities under the pseudonym Sister Outrider. She reads one of a trio of essays addressed to white feminists, entitled 'To The White Women Who Want To Know How To Be My Friend'. The name Sister Outrider is a reference to Audre Lourde and the essay title paraphrases the Black poet   Pat Parker's 1978 poem.

Heuchan's talk is not a question or a plea, or even a suggestion. It is a statement of fact addressed to all the white women in the room. She goes on to run an exercise in recognising your allies, getting everyone to examine their own allyship and asking how they can be better.

INTER SECTION ALITY

When cracks appear in movements that seem to be striving for the same thing, they usually happen along intersectional fault lines.

Failure to address intersections of class and race, sexuality, gender identity, disability and neurodivergence can divide the groups who need each other's solidarity the most.

Penguins survive brutual winters by huddling together in rotation in huge colonies. We must remember that even if we've fought hard to get safe and warm in the midst of this Arctic wasteland of capitalist patriarchy...

...we must be vigilant that we are also making space for those even more vulnerable and marginalised, not only to simply survive, but to thrive.

The term intersectionality was first coined by Kimberlé Crenshaw. A Black woman and scholar of critical race theory, she developed the concept at college in the early '80s.

'SAY HER NAME'

She discovered a dearth of research examining how race, sex, gender and class literally intersect, affecting the human experience within society.

AIYANA STANLEY-JONES

AURA ROSSER

MYA HALL

KAYLA MOORE

MIRIAM CAREY

MICHELLE CUSSEAUX

ALBERTA SPRUILL

TANISHA ANDERSON

SHELLY FREY.

Whilst researching Crenshaw, the Beast found that she was heavily involved in the 'Say Her Name' project.

PEARLIE GOLDEN

A sister protest to Black Lives Matter, 'Say Her Name' aims to elevate women who have lost their lives at the hands of police and state violence. These are just a few of the victims we should remember.

The Beast meets activist Lizzie and artist Jesse Jones at Shifting Loyalties.

1967: the Abortion Act U.K. is passed.

1970: Roe vs. Wade makes abortion in the U.S. constitutional.

1970: In Ireland married couples are allowed contraception.

These landmark rulings were huge steps forward for reproductive rights in these countries. So what happened in Ireland, and what is 'Repeal' referring to?

REPEAL

REPEAL

As laws concerning freedoms around sex began to be gradually relaxed from the '60s onward, public attitudes and the pressure from the Church doubled down to prevent such an unacceptable erosion of the moral fabric of society. In 1983, one of these fire and brimstone campaigns was a referendum to vote on the 8th Amendment, which would give the foetus the same rights to life as the mother. It passed.

In 2012 Savita Halappanavar died when the hospital she was admitted to refused her a termination, even though her life was in danger. This kickstarted a huge, united movement, 'Repeal the 8th', culminating in a referendum in 2017.

Proudly wearing her 'Repeal' sweater to spread the message, Jesse runs a clay workshop. To honour the sheela na gig - a little vulva-flashing stone cutie found throughout Europe - she gets the group to sculpt lips, clits and vaginas, which they do with great aplomb.

Rahila Gupta addresses the room, again talking about her recent trip to Rojava. Silvia Federici goes on to compare Rojava to the Zapatista rebellion in Chiapas, Mexico, in the early '90s. The rebels made use of the fledgling internet to appeal to global organisations outside their government, to shift the power back to the indigenous population.

Both movements are also women-centered. The Zapatista's 'Women's Law' made demands for the female population to have autonomy over their bodies, hold positions of power within the community, and to live a life free from fear of violence.

When indigenous people rise up against oppression...

...with a focus on women and the environment...

...it is everyone else's time to step down and support them.

DINNERBEES

In between intense talk of intersectionality and revolution there is time.

Time for long walks in the hills.

102

Time for Silvia Federici to mash potatoes like a boss, and time for the Beast to make too much TVP mince.

LIZZIE + JESSE SHARE BREAKFAST SANDWICHES WITH THE BEAST IN MUDDY FIELDS.

AND SCATTERED IN THE FIELDS ARE THE WEIGHT LIFTING RUMINANTS...

THE SHAPE SHIFTING GRAZERS...

ARE THEY COWS? NO SILVIA. NO. THEY ARE JUST VERY LARGE SHEEP.

(THE BEAST CONTINUES)

SO 6 PACKS OF TVP AND THIRTY OF US... (BAD MATHS HAPPENS...)

(TO HAVE NO IDEA)

I'LL JUST USE ALL OF IT ....

(WHAT SHE'S DOING)

uh oh...

LIFE!

IS THE MINCE READY?

YES! (READY TO DESTROY US ALL...)

And time to observe and appreciate the delicately tuned tools for making chapatis.

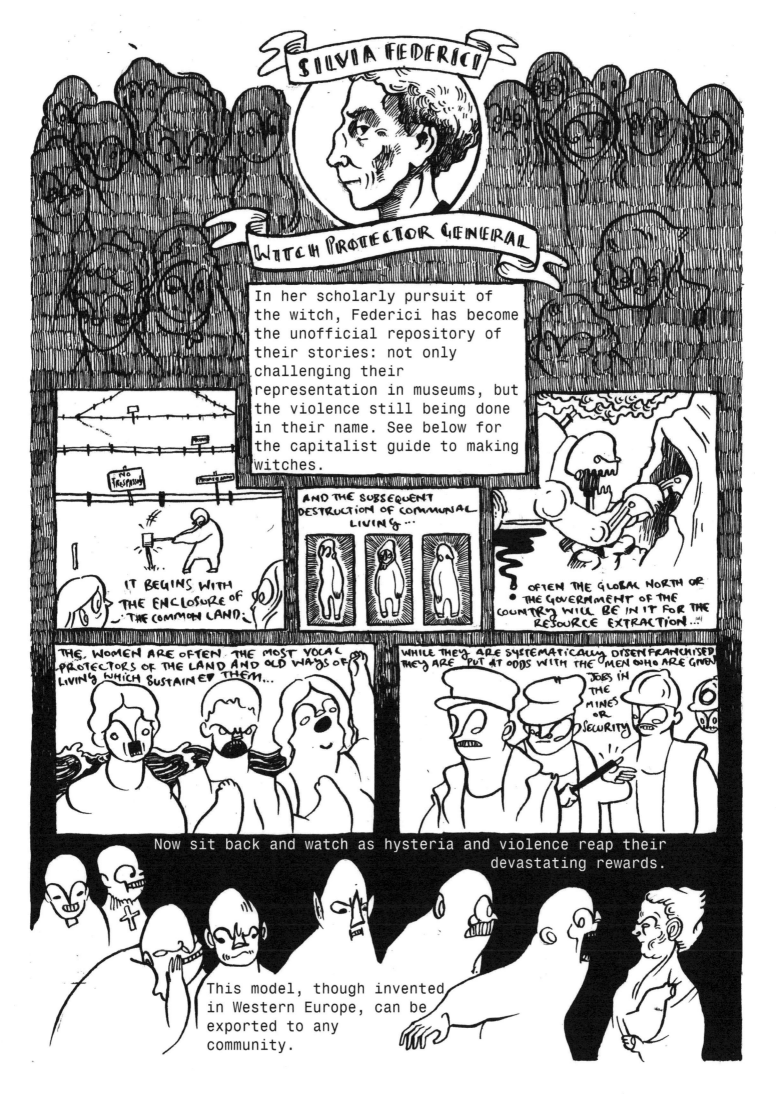

Of their appearance across post-colonial Africa, Silvia Federici writes: 'These witch hunts are not a legacy of the past, but a response to the social crisis the globalisation and neo-liberal restructuring of Africa's political economies has produced.'

She summarises scholar Justus Ogembo's argument, 'that the proliferation of fundamental sects, re-injecting religion with a fear of the devil, and by the appearance of self-defined 'traditional healers', exploiting people's inability to pay hospital fees are the true makers of the witch.'

The propaganda machine that directs this fear and hatred towards women...

...is alive and well in museums all over the world...

...reducing gendercide and oppression to a diorama of Halloween novelties.

The Beast finds an article in Vice on a 'Witch Camp' in Northern Ghana. These 'witches' are often widows with no right to inheritance or property, elderly women, or women with children who have no access to the ways and means of supporting themselves. In support of Federici's theory, this is persecution as an economic solution, predominantly targeting and punishing women.

The Beast has two excellent room mates. The first is photographer and filmmaker Kajal Nisha Patel.

Kajal documents the British Indian diaspora, from those who fled Idi Amin's Uganda, to the economic migrants who joined the post-war British workforce. While her previous work was primarily photographic, she's currently making a series of short films, '4 Women, 5 Stories', using the extensive archives at Leicester University.

Kajal found her subjects because they were all involved in the late '70s Grunwick dispute, which was predominantly led by women of colour. The women, however, were reluctant to talk about the dispute, so instead, her films are quiet portraits of loneliness, alienation, hostility and camaraderie set against backdrops of ordinary domesticity.

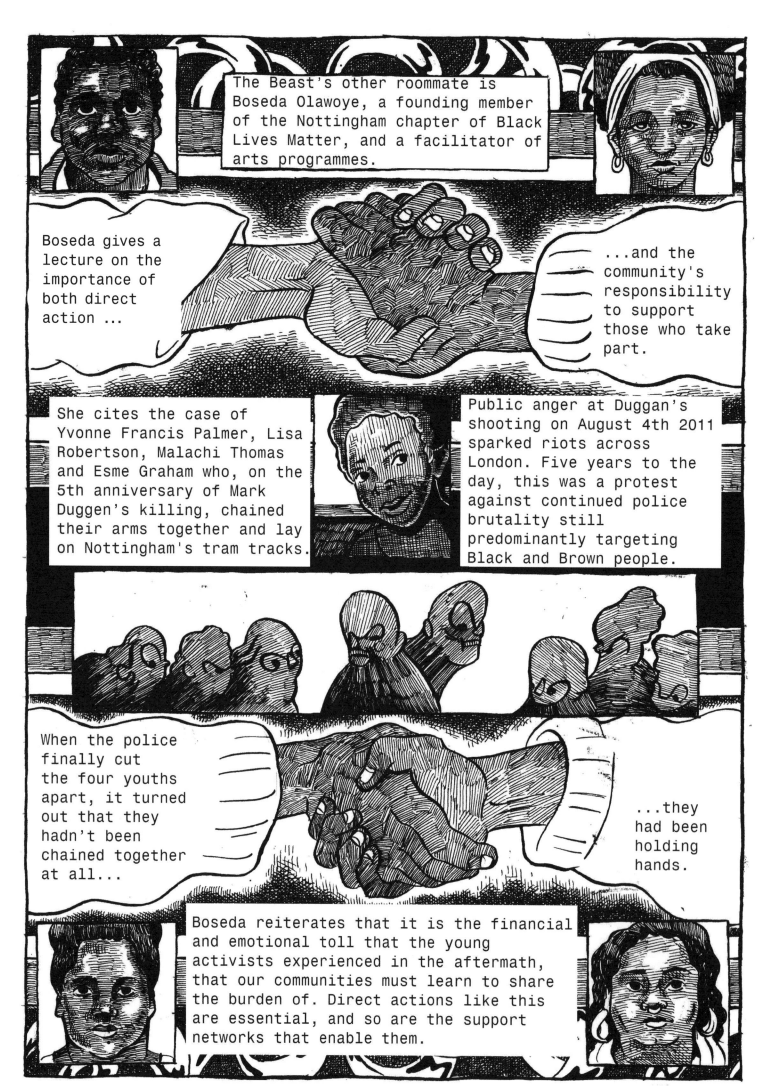

The Beast's other roommate is Boseda Olawoye, a founding member of the Nottingham chapter of Black Lives Matter, and a facilitator of arts programmes.

Boseda gives a lecture on the importance of both direct action ...

...and the community's responsibility to support those who take part.

She cites the case of Yvonne Francis Palmer, Lisa Robertson, Malachi Thomas and Esme Graham who, on the 5th anniversary of Mark Duggen's killing, chained their arms together and lay on Nottingham's tram tracks.

Public anger at Duggan's shooting on August 4th 2011 sparked riots across London. Five years to the day, this was a protest against continued police brutality still predominantly targeting Black and Brown people.

When the police finally cut the four youths apart, it turned out that they hadn't been chained together at all...

...they had been holding hands.

Boseda reiterates that it is the financial and emotional toll that the young activists experienced in the aftermath, that our communities must learn to share the burden of. Direct actions like this are essential, and so are the support networks that enable them.

Towards the end of the Conference there is an opportunity to break off into smaller groups. Uzma runs a storytelling night in Bradford, and is trying to forge a career in the arts under the baffled gaze of her family.

UZMA

Uzma wants to discuss whether it's possible to resolve conflicting beliefs within our own communities, like trying to tell her grandmother why it isn't okay to refuse to visit her in hospital if she ever gave birth to a baby girl.

We look for connection through commonality.

Taking something we hold dear, to those we believe will understand us, only to find that...

...for whatever reason they have sided with the oppressor.

Those with all the power and resources do not need our solidarity, and they are able to ensure we remain in precarious states. This means we need each other.

The family we are born into is not always safe.

Nor are the institutions we are made to pass through, or the relationships we are pressured to form.

We struggle to find and build community and family outside these divisive social constructions...

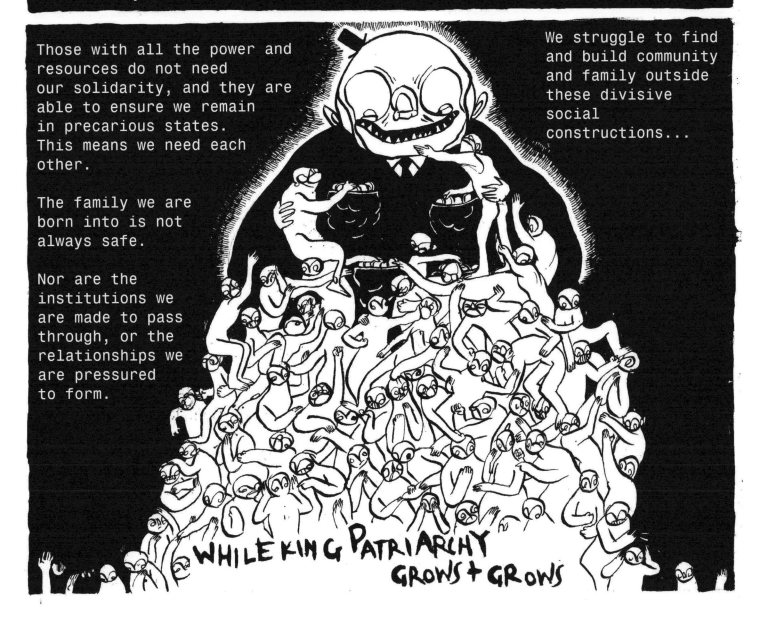

WHILE KING PATRIARCHY GROWS + GROWS

The Shifting Loyalties Conference seems to be asking...

...if women gather with a collective interest...

...can differences be overcome for a common purpose?

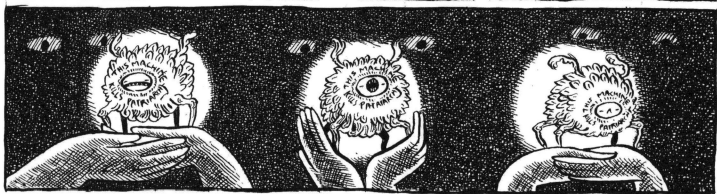

The Beast doesn't know. And for a dark moment it seems as though the only thing women have in common across all our intersecting differences, is violence.

Can we learn to talk to one another? More importantly, can we learn to listen and dismantle white supremacy, patriarchy and capitalism for good?

Not all of us are oppressed by the same enemy and we know that not all will experience oppression in the same way.

'I am not free while any woman is unfree. Even if her shackles are very different from mine.'

Audre Lorde, writer and poet.

It seems like a long time has passed since the Beast arrived at Coldwell with two other strangers in the inky dark of a midwinter evening.

The world outside the taxi was reduced to a few feet of visibility, the ghost of a monochrome dreamscape.

The women leave in daylight, the wild Lancashire countryside rolling and dipping dramatically like a revelation. The Beast thinks:

Perhaps human connections and lived experience are headlights in the dark; each new one is like the dawn coming up, and revealing a slightly more complex and beautiful whole.

Selina Cooper was built for covert gatherings. She is a shifting, secret space. She is not passive, and will hopefully evolve with all who experience her.

Idle Women will not be together again until the Spring. The break is well earned and much-needed. The Beast catches a train home with clothes full of woodsmoke and a head full of excited noise.

SPRING 2017

MIRFIELD, W. YORKSHIRE

The day after Trump's inauguration there are women's marches all over the world. The new president announces a travel ban against seven majority Muslim countries. People are stranded at airports, and asylum processes that many have spent years and everything they have on applying for, are destroyed.

The murmur will rise to a roar under this oppressive and regressive regime.

It is an underground murmur, like a kind of tinnitus.

It is the sound of the witches.

They are coming.

The Beast arrives in Yorkshire.

A new year. A new mooring. A new canal.

Same old locals.

The Beast sits on Adelaide's nose waiting for Cis and Rachel to arrive.

She has spent the last three months writing this graphic novel and delving deep into Winter madness. Tomorrow, Idle Women launches a new season and artist residency. Finally, Cis and Rachel appear on the towpath.

They talk Winter over tea.

Rachel's mum arrives to help out with tomorrow's event.

Plans are made over fish and chips.

Rachel drives the Beast to her petrol station motel.

They get lost in conversation, lit by the headlights.

And run the car battery down.

This year, Idle Women's Spring launch coincides with International Women's Day, a global day of power and resistance born of women-led revolution, protest and civil disobedience. It was made official by the U.N. (thanks, we were going to celebrate anyway, actually) as International Women's Rights and World Peace Day. Funny that they see the two things as synonymous, but the former are still fighting for basic human rights in many places.

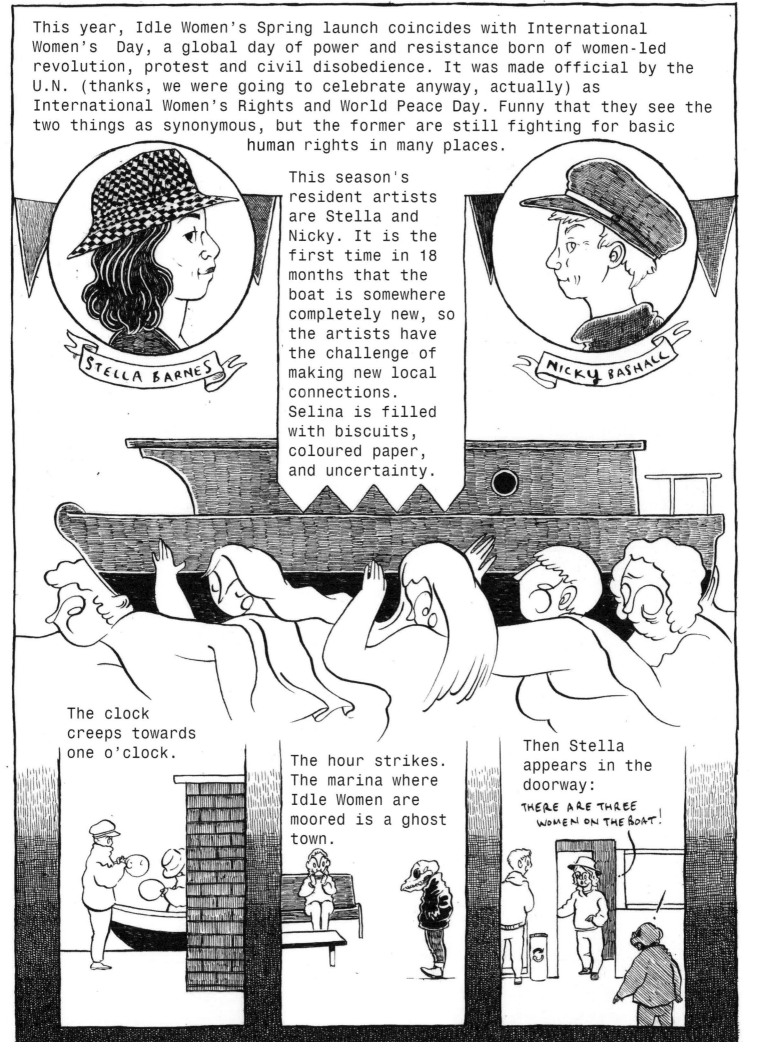

This season's resident artists are Stella and Nicky. It is the first time in 18 months that the boat is somewhere completely new, so the artists have the challenge of making new local connections. Selina is filled with biscuits, coloured paper, and uncertainty.

STELLA BARNES

NICKY BASHALL

The clock creeps towards one o'clock.

The hour strikes. The marina where Idle Women are moored is a ghost town.

Then Stella appears in the doorway:

THERE ARE THREE WOMEN ON THE BOAT!

Local women gather on Selina for the first time.

Hands shape paper into delicate vessels.

Selina fills up with boats covered in felt tip wisdom.

The Beast takes a break from meeting new humans.

She passes a group of men trying not to take up space.

She goes in search of the one vegan flavour of pie.

She is not subtle.

Selina is moored at a place called Shepley Bridge where the canal presses its slight nose against the fierce flank of the River Calder. The evening rolls in, and Stella and Nicky get the women to rename the Calder. The river collects the new appellations eagerly; the dead, the beloved, the invisible, and the ridiculous.

3 Poems

A raucous celebration of hairy female bodies.

A song of love and longing in Urdu.

A life sunk deep in depression.

When the third reader finishes her poem about depression, the woman who sang the Urdu poems turns to her, moved to tears, and says that she has been looking for those words inside herself for a long time. And found them here.

The first day is done.

118

Between visits to Yorkshire, the Beast meets Idle Women in London.

They are marching with the Million Women Rise rally.

The Beast spots Lizzie who's drumming in a samba band.

Moj is there too, still on crutches, and together they march from Oxford Street to Trafalgar Square.

This is Million Women Rise's 10th year. Black-led, grassroots and inspired by movements in the Democratic Republic of Congo and Palestine, Sabrina Qureshi started it when, working as a counsellor, she saw a lot of women who were victims of domestic and sexual violence. She felt like an island of care in a sea of governmental and societal indifference. On the estate where she grew up, violence against women was so unremarkable it was rendered invisible. She hopes that by changing society, hearts and minds:

TOGETHER WE CAN END MALE VIOLENCE AGAINST WOMEN

It is Social time again, and this time Idle Women have use of the activity centre at the marina. They have baked approximately one million potatoes for six women. Those present tell stories by way of introduction:

As a teenager, Stella worked in a factory, rolling towels and enduring rampant sexism.

The locker room was a hub of black market trading from Tupperware to sex toys.

Rachel and Cis have had trouble ...

...getting the residents of Shepley Bridge to grant them access to the marina.

From getting keys, to using the community hall, this Bridge has trolls, and they hate sharing.

Parveen has just given birth, and she's fighting with her mother-in-law who is arranging the traditonal sacrifice of a goat for the feast to bless the child.

This is the first act of a rebellion that will change Parveen's life completely.

NO! NO! NO! NO!

I DON'T KNOW. THESE MODERN WOMEN...I JUST DON'T UNDERSTAND THEM...

There are not enough potatoes to talk about opiates and crossing Iran. Everyone is full of carbs and good company.

The Beast meets Parveen just as her life is going through some seismic changes.

Parveen is a poet. At the launch she reads a cheeky little verse about illicitly cutting her hair as a child.

120

Raised in a strict Sikh household, this was no small display of childish autonomy.

In the last 18 months, Parveen has also cut away a marriage and a well-paid job.

She is on a new path, attempting to live a life more aligned with her own ideals and beliefs, her heart and head hungry for knowledge and new ways of being.

One of the catalysts for these changes was her daughter Arooje. In order to raise her boldly, she must live her truth.

The Beast stays with Parveen on the night of the Social. Arooje introduces her to her current favourite Bollywood film, 'Gulaab Gang', based on the true story of Sampat Pal and her women's vigilante group from Uttar Pradesh, India.

Known as the Pink Gang for the colours of their saris, and as formidable seekers of justice for the colour of their actions, the film is pretty fierce. The Beast wishes she had been this cool when she was five.

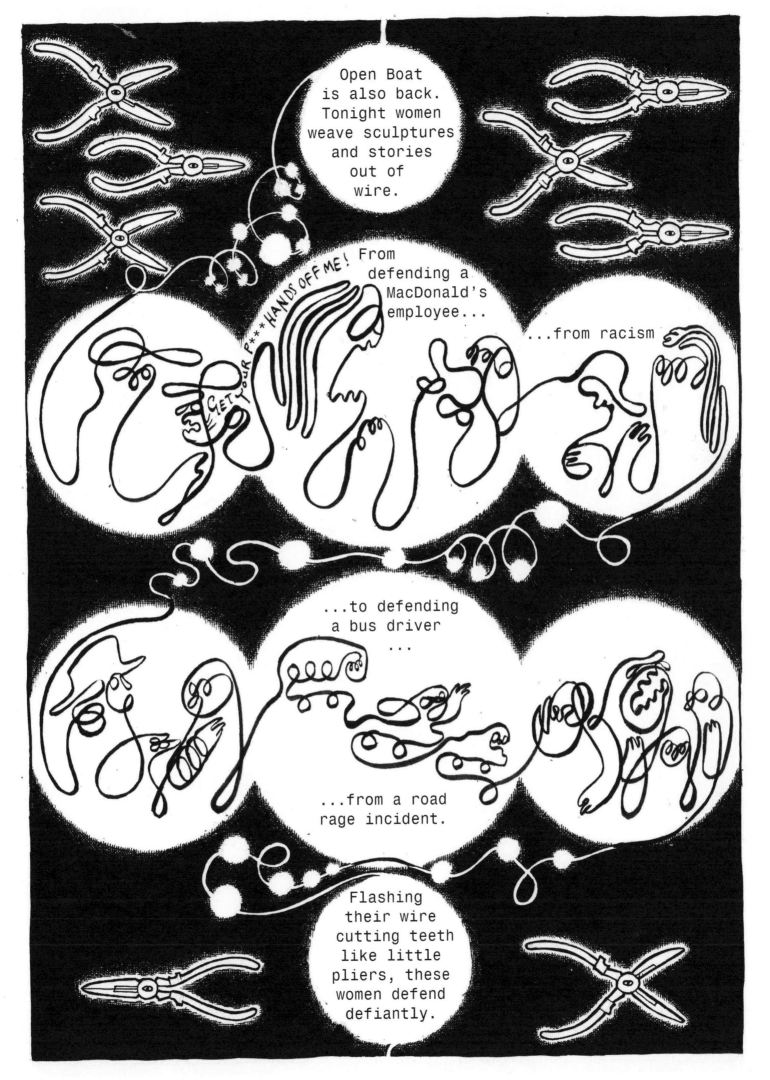

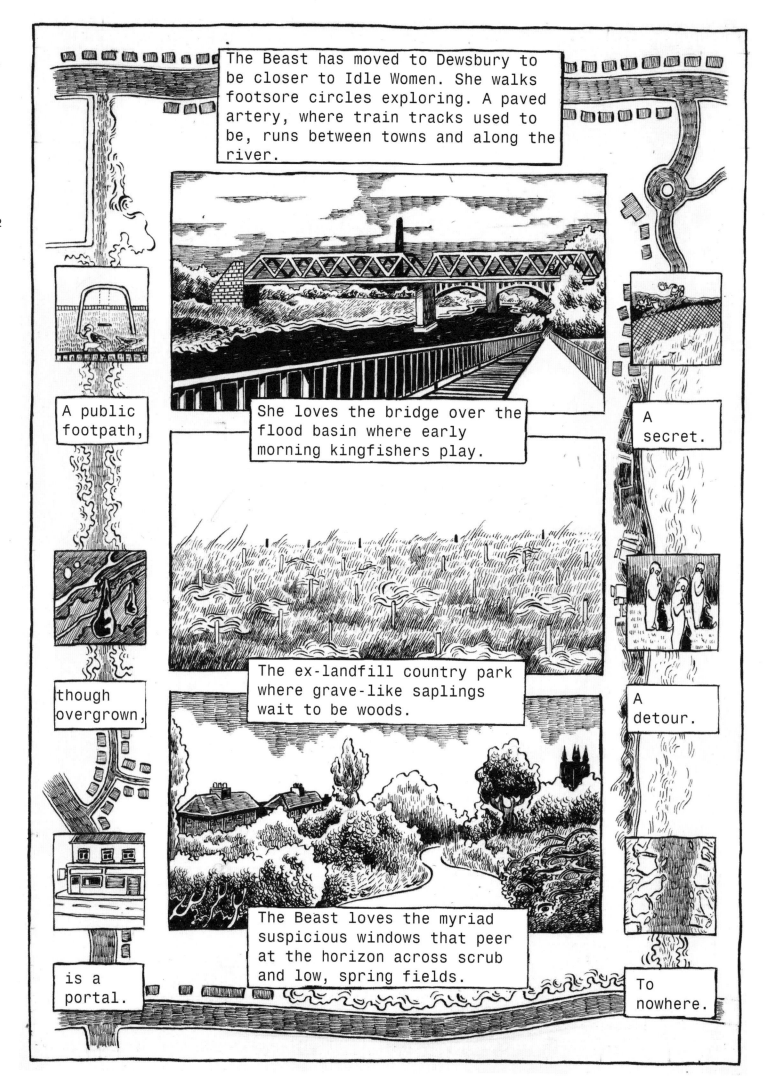

The Beast has moved to Dewsbury to be closer to Idle Women. She walks footsore circles exploring. A paved artery, where train tracks used to be, runs between towns and along the river.

A public footpath,

She loves the bridge over the flood basin where early morning kingfishers play.

A secret.

though overgrown,

The ex-landfill country park where grave-like saplings wait to be woods.

A detour.

is a portal.

The Beast loves the myriad suspicious windows that peer at the horizon across scrub and low, spring fields.

To nowhere.

124

The Social that week is spaghetti, hand dancing, and silliness.

Between Idle Women's work with local groups and word of mouth, Selina's presence is becoming known, and many women attend that night.

It is new growth after a long Winter.

That night Cis and Rachel are leaving to take a few days off. After last year's Black Root burnout they are going to try harder to look after themselves and have asked the Beast to stay on Adelaide.

At first, every creak and knock sets the Beast on edge. But a kettle, a fire, and a cat soon make the boat feel like a friendly fortress, impervious to everything.

LOOKS LIKE ITS JUST YOU AND ME NOW, HELEN.

Well, almost everything.

CUNTS!
(HA HA HA)

CUNTS!
(HA!)

(et cetera...)

Spring brings blackthorn buds and a glorious dawn chorus to the canal, and while they are neighbours, the Beast gets to know Stella and Nicky better.

They are both working artists and arts facilitators...

...often involved in projects with migrant children and refugees...

...untangling the knots of their experiences into poetry and theatre.

Some of these children have grown up to develop strong creative practices of their own, now living and working as writers, artists and activists. Stella tells the Beast that she has attended one of their weddings, and it is clear that both she and Nicky forge strong bonds with the communities they work with.

The artists also try to use their time on Selina to develop their own projects. One afternoon, the Beast and Nicky are having tea. 'I tried to write today', Nicky tells her. 'But I was too tired.' You wouldn't know it to work with her, but following a serious illness a few years ago, Nicky began suffering from chronic fatigue.

A spectre, who can make even moving a pen across a page unbearably heavy.

THE SOCIAL DIVIDED part 1

As if the country wasn't divided enough, Theresa May announces an election.

"It is time to tighten our stranglehold ..."

"In times of crisis, the people should decide..."

The Social is strange that night. Dewsbury's Labour MP Paula Sherriff is attending with some of Idle Women's creative partners.

Visiting constituents is important, but no one really knows what to say. So we just politely eat our bangers and mash.

It feels a bit like having to be on your best behaviour when people visit your classroom.

Earlier that day, Rachel showed the Beast the saplings she and Cis will take to St Helen's on Sunday, for a parallel project ahead of the tour's arrival in the town later in the year. The saplings look so peaceful and uncomplicated, and the Beast wants to curl up next to them and go to sleep.

DEWSBURY

This ex-mill town is trying to find itself in the post-industrial world.

In the centre is what used to be a grand market, like the one still very much alive in Leeds. The women the Beast talks to are frustrated that the council won't invest in it again.

HALIFAX

BRADFORD

DEWSBURY MARKET

HUDDERSFIELD

WAKEFIELD

LEEDS

The new money is going into college buildings with all the roads named after places you leave Dewsbury for.

Like often happens in small towns, it is both multicultural and segregated.

All woven through with tow paths, canals and tumbling rivers...

...where the dog-day Summer swallows become Halloween bats at dusk.

The Beast is waiting for Cis and Rachel to pick her up so they can go to a play in Leeds. An abandoned building is on fire opposite her house, and she stands with the teenagers and kids watching the fire service put it out with surgical precision.

The play is called 'The Darkest Corners'. The theatre is a car park and the audience wear headphones.

It is a musical about a woman walking alone at night, with little vignettes of violence playing out around her.

Catcalls echo and intimate partner violence is whispered...

COULD WE STOP?

(BUT YOU PROMISED...

...straight into our ears.

There is a song for avenging angel Diana, killer of the bus drivers who raped women in Mexico.

Sampat Pal's Gulaab Gang appear, backlit by headlights and wielding lathis.

There is one monologue on violence where the Beast almost takes her headphones off. The moment the thought crosses her mind, a woman in front of her actually does. There are some things you don't need to be told again.

Stella and Nicky have been doing group work at the women's centre. Today, they've invited the women on to Selina to craft a tree.

The Beast works with one of the women on the tow path, who tells her that while she was picnicking in a field with her partner...

...they found a little stone marker. It was the site of a pit collapse and when they looked it up later, the woman found that her uncle-in-law had died in it.

The Beast realises she's neglected the area's mining history in her research, and looks into it a little. She discovers that before the mid-19th century women and children had frequently worked in the mines.

Because their labour was cheaper, men petitioned to have the women removed so they could demand better pay. Women became 'bad luck'.

Much like in the factories (and the whole world), women were often expected to come home from the mine...

...and look after the household.

Voices and stories are not lost. They are wilfully buried.

It takes work to excavate the bones of the women's stories and rebuild them into people.

But it is work that is both rewarding and necessary.

In theme with this idea, the Beast recalls two authors she read recently.

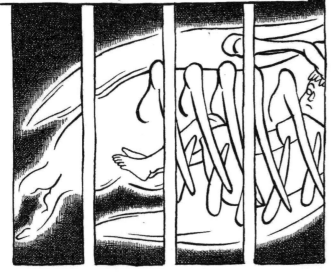

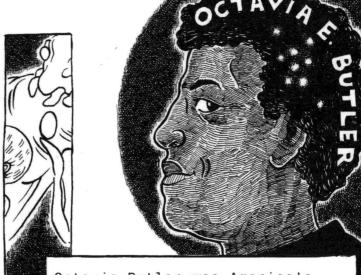

OCTAVIA E. BUTLER

Octavia Butler was America's first widely celebrated Black female science fiction writer.

In a collection of short stories; a boy lies in the arms of the insect whose larvae he will one day carry, and in a world that has lost all language, one woman alone retains it.

Butler's characters are often without overt power, but are secretly subversive. They must hide, shapeshift and be cunning in order to survive.

Butler writes like she knows the worst that can happen.

And asks her characters:

"What will you do now?"

And they always answer with an action.

Her stories often span lifetimes and sometimes generations. You can fight hard and fast to win a battle.

But patience, work, and constant vigilance is required if you're going to win the war.

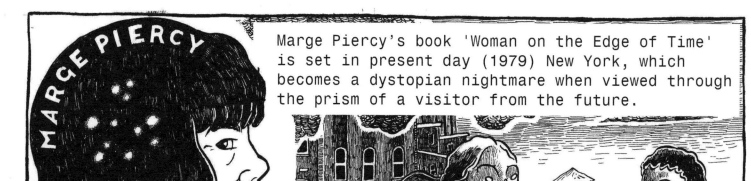

MARGE PIERCY

Marge Piercy's book 'Woman on the Edge of Time' is set in present day (1979) New York, which becomes a dystopian nightmare when viewed through the prism of a visitor from the future.

Jumping between the present and the past, Piercy critiques mental health institutions, a violent gender binary, and systemic racism.

Her protagonist is seduced and abandoned by her professor.

Her partner dies in the experimental drug trial he's put on in lieu of parole.

Her child is taken away, and disappears into the care system.

And finally, her niece's pimp has her committed to an asylum.

Luciente comes from a future still carefully recovering from our reckless and destructive industrial age.

Centuries of women-led revolution have degendered everything, from language to childcare.

When children come of age they mark it by choosing new names; which may continue to change as they grow.

Relationships are not anchored in ownership. Sexual preferences and long term intimacies may emerge, but nothing is fixed.

Like Butler, Piercy has her characters perform actions, the results of which they may never see.

And when she finishes the book, the Beast misses that future world like a home she can never go back to.

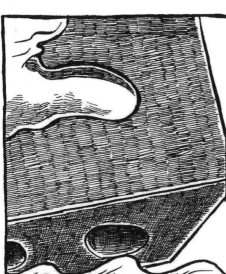

West of Selina, Idle Women are laying the foundations for 'Bricks and Mortar', the project in St. Helens that will follow the tour. In partnership with two new arts organisations, they have started to work with a domestic violence refuge.

When the Beast arrives Cis, Rachel and the women residents, with the help of YouTube, are teaching themselves to build walls. But the atmosphere is tense...

Rachel and Cis receive word that someone tried to break into Adelaide last night.

Unable to go and check on their home, Rachel and Cis hope for the best while trying to prepare for the worst.

The shelter is mixed gender, and Rachel and Cis have reiterated that the work they're doing is with women only. The one man in the group will not step back and let the women take up the space.

The women are divided into the one who defends him... and everybody else.

The shelter is poorly funded. In order to care for the people it houses, who often have complex needs, it is run a little bit like a prison.

Rachel, who has done work like this for a long time, says it isn't Idle Women's job to change the space. But to provide an alternative one.

The Beast finds Cis among those newly planted trees.

Just painting a playhouse has made the place feel better...

"Think of what fifty grand could do here...", she sighs.

Over breakfast on the last day one of the artists, Louise Lowe, tells the Beast about a production she worked on called 'Laundry'.

It was about the Magdalene Laundries, which were effectively church-run workhouses for so-called 'fallen women' in Ireland.

In 1993, when the nuns sold some land belonging to one of the laundries, a mass grave was discovered where 133 bodies had been buried. There was a national outcry, and the last laundry was closed in 1996.

'Laundry' was a site-specific immersive theatre piece, set in one of the old buildings, and based on interviews with some of the few survivors. The Beast notes that institutional abuse in return for free labour is becoming a new theme.

Raksha Patel arrives that evening to join tomorrow's work. The Beast sits between conversations about sin-eaters and tepid government funded art; future projects and past failures.

There is a happy feeling of homecoming riding the slow train back to Blackburn. The Beast passes many of last year's haunts.

Even though they've moved to Yorkshire, Idle Women have maintained their relationship with Humraaz. But with irregular sessions and the turnover of women at Humraaz, it hasn't been easy.

Still, the women show up, and this time Cis and Rachel are bringing the bricklaying knowledge they learned with the women in St. Helens, to a small church car park in Blackburn.

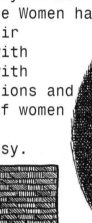 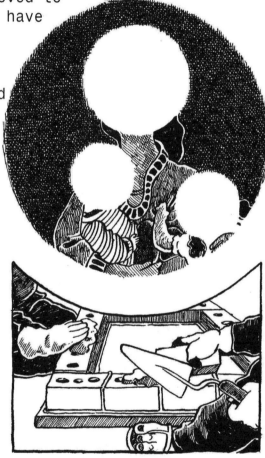 

The women are sceptical at first.

But soon become completely engrossed in the task at hand.

Taking it in turns to build a wall.

Even one of the women who has been disruptive in the sessions, is today one of the last to leave.

Idle Women bring all the fixings for a pizza night at the Social, and the family of Madhia, a friend of project, provide biryani.

139

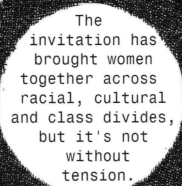
The invitation has brought women together across racial, cultural and class divides, but it's not without tension.

Cis and Rachel are still tired from St. Helens. One of the women from Stella and Nicky's group argues with her mum.

There are quite a few kids present who are a lot more at ease in the space than their adults...

...reminding the Beast of uncomplicated beautfiul things...
TABBY'S MOON!
·OH ! YEAH.

...and the joy of pure anarchy.

That night on Selina, Stella is giving a crash course in fairytales

and their problematic

...portrayals of women.

YOU'RE NOT OUR MUM.

TELL ME ABOUT IT. MY FAMILY SOLD ME TO YOUR DAD.

Through story telling and song, Stella and Nicky teach both structure and narrative subversion.

Then they get the group to split into pairs to write their own stories.

Stella and Nicky have been working with the group, Mother's Apart From Their Children. One of the women in particular has really embraced the workshops and attends every session, even if she can't always take part.

The woman shares the skills she's learned and objects she's made, when visiting her kids.

The story she creates that evening is sophisticated and funny.

A girl defies her fairy godmother and accidentally turns herself into a wolf.

She steals a magic book, and after a few failures, turns herself back.

The fairy finds out what she did, but instead of being angry, tells the girl she's proud of her for learning magic.

BUILDING STORIES

BUILDING BOATS

In her search for adventure stories centering women, Nicky finds a Yurok legend about Umai, who journeys to the horizon and falls in love with a woman, only to leave again, homesick for her people.

Restlessness and longing strike resonant chords with all the women that night.

Many of them are trying to rebuild lives and families. They tell adventure stories...

...of grandmothers fleeing political strife, and mothers escaping abusive relationships.

Everyone who has found Selina seems to have a longing within herself.

The paper boats folded on that first day become sturdy wooden vessels.

The session ends with the usually sassy Heidi reading a heartfelt poem about how Stella and Nicky's presence has affected her. This is the last Open Boat, and the imminent ending weighs heavy on them all.

That week, Cis and Rachel are away at the Venice Biennale.

Where the art machine is at its most unbearable.

They're at the Biennale to support Jesse Jones, who the Beast met at Coldwell. Jesse is representing Ireland with her monolithic installation 'Tremble Tremble'.

Jesse fills a room with a huge projection of a giantess. Working with a herbalist, an olfactory element is added, immersing the audience in the giantess's presence.

Jesse's work wants to celebrate women as the origin of life, so she confronts the capitalist patriarchy in the midst of this sinking city with the chant: "Tremate, tremate, le streghe sono tornate!"*

*"Tremble, tremble, the witches have returned."

Among the last big events of that Spring, is one Stella and Nicky have organised with a group of Muslim women at Ravensthorpe Library. The women came up with the theme of 'hands' as emblems of work, creativity and care.

They blend their own essential oils into hand cream.

Parveen helps them to make flags from fabric scraps.

They cover boxes in delicately embossed foil, heads bowed in concentration.

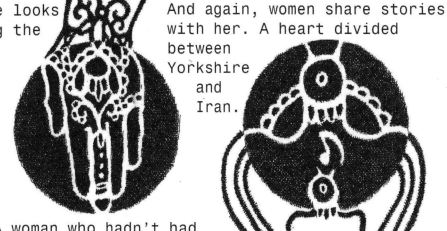

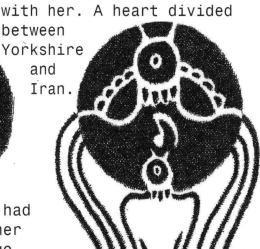

The Beast is given henna. She looks at it doubtfully, remembering the Seed Bombs.

And again, women share stories with her. A heart divided between Yorkshire and Iran.

A woman who hadn't had Mehndi done since her wedding 24 years ago.

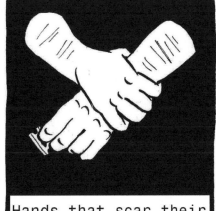

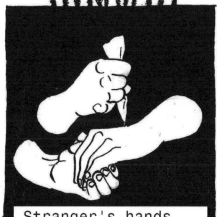

Hands that clean children's faces.

Hands that scar their own bodies.

Stranger's hands, holding each other tightly.

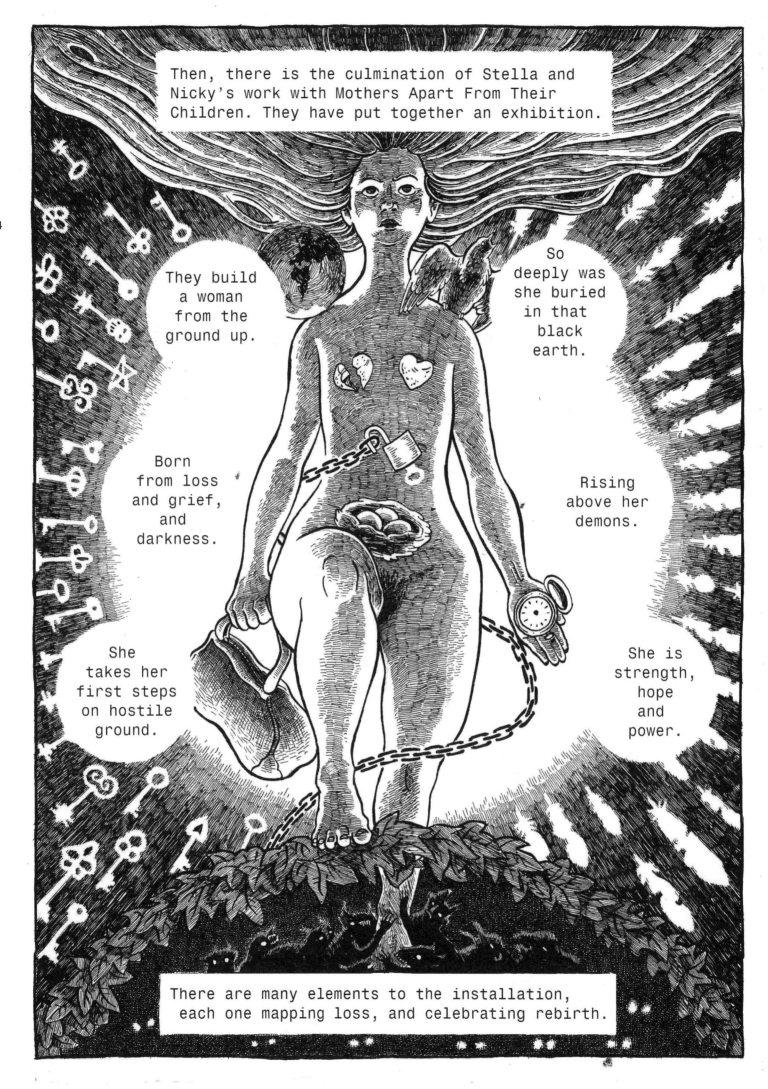

Then, quite suddenly, on the last day of Stella and Nicky's residency, it is Summer. The final Social is out on the tow path and women from the Spring's adventures gather together.

Rose is passing on her boat-building skills to her nephew.

A woman from the library group is soliciting divorce advice from Parveen and Heidi.

One of the women from Mothers Apart took at least two buses and a couple of hours to get here.

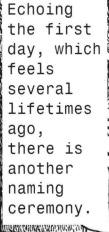

Echoing the first day, which feels several lifetimes ago, there is another naming ceremony.

This time, the women name their rafts. Three of them are called 'Rachel', and there's also 'Skeletor', which amuses the Beast no end.

Three months is no time at all. It feels like the work is just beginning. Stella and Nicky aren't ready to leave.

Summer 2017

MIRFIELD, W. YORKSHIRE

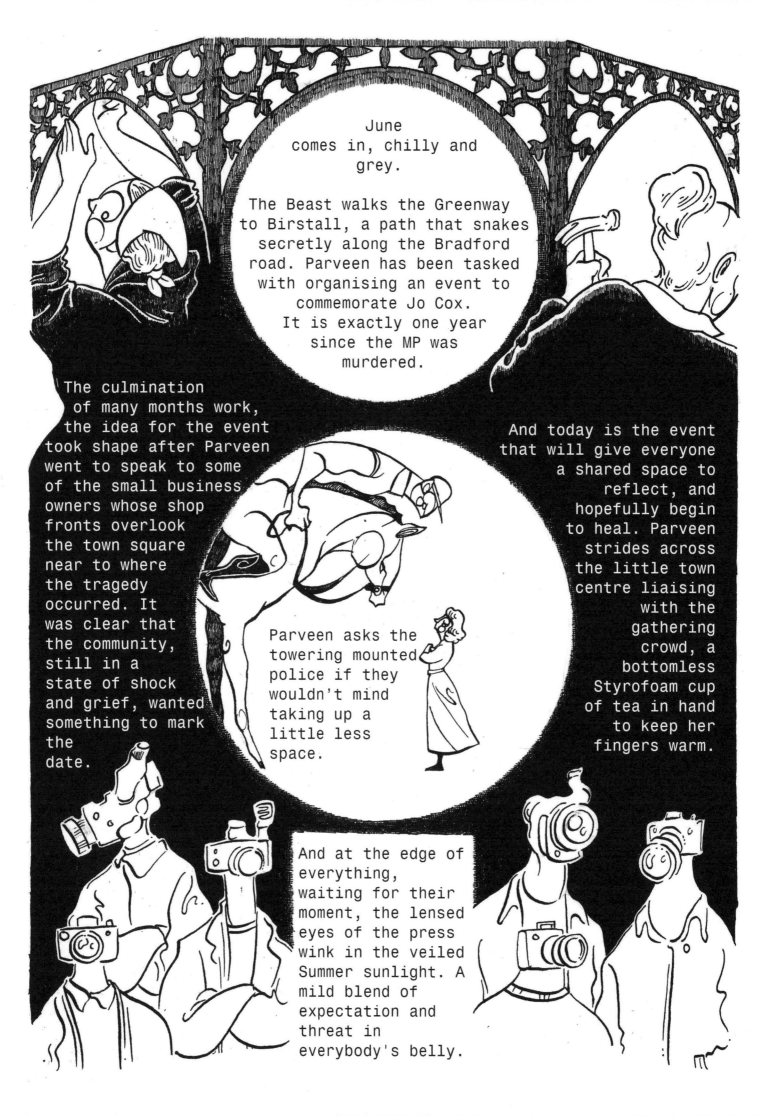

June comes in, chilly and grey.

The Beast walks the Greenway to Birstall, a path that snakes secretly along the Bradford road. Parveen has been tasked with organising an event to commemorate Jo Cox. It is exactly one year since the MP was murdered.

The culmination of many months work, the idea for the event took shape after Parveen went to speak to some of the small business owners whose shop fronts overlook the town square near to where the tragedy occurred. It was clear that the community, still in a state of shock and grief, wanted something to mark the date.

Parveen asks the towering mounted police if they wouldn't mind taking up a little less space.

And today is the event that will give everyone a shared space to reflect, and hopefully begin to heal. Parveen strides across the little town centre liaising with the gathering crowd, a bottomless Styrofoam cup of tea in hand to keep her fingers warm.

And at the edge of everything, waiting for their moment, the lensed eyes of the press wink in the veiled Summer sunlight. A mild blend of expectation and threat in everybody's belly.

A blue gazebo goes up at the edge of the square. Crepe paper flowers in suffragette white, green and purple begin to bloom. School children sing to the gathered crowd.

A friend of Parveen's recalls the moment she heard about Jo Cox's murder. The first social media tremors. Rushing into town because her daughter was at school near to where the perpetrator was taken down. She tells it slowly, quietly.

Then after the speeches and official commemorative business, the crowd seems to let out a collective exhalation. The police are making paper flowers, and school children run around, enjoying their freedom.

It's been a good day.

The spell of Spring is broken. Idle Women gather on a drizzly tow path to say a final farewell to Stella and Nicky. While Cis and Rachel are lighting the BBQ, a group of teenage boys crowd up. Their words are innocuous, but their body language is aggressive.

It's an unwelcome reminder of the kind of energy the canal can foster. And it's also manifesting in the escalating hostility of the men Idle Women share the marina with. Micro-aggressions have become simply aggressions, and tensions are running high.

The men have been flouting boating etiquette and driving, instead of coasting, past Idle Women's moored boats. Cis and Rachel have tried to confront them or at least start an email exchange, but the men have ignored everything. Those who hold the power in these situations usually get to choose whether or not they engage, a privilege not afforded to Cis and Rachel.

Then when the women do finally lose their tempers, it is the men who are outraged.

They compain directly to Idle Women's partners and the situation reaches an impasse.

The first blow of the Summer comes when the next stage of Selina's tour to Manchester falls through, and the boat must remain in Mirfield.

Rachel and Cis pull together a last minute Summer programme by inviting women to apply to stay on Selina, and in return share skills with local women.

The first is Linda Grieve. She works in stained glass, and shows the group how to use strange tools to manipulate sharp shards of colour.

Linda teaches techniques like 'nibbling', to make shapes fit together, as seen on old lead-lined church windows. The snapping glass sets the Beast's teeth on edge.

In the early days of Selina's construction, a communication error led her to be built with an errant porthole that Cis and Rachel have long intended to fill with stained glass.

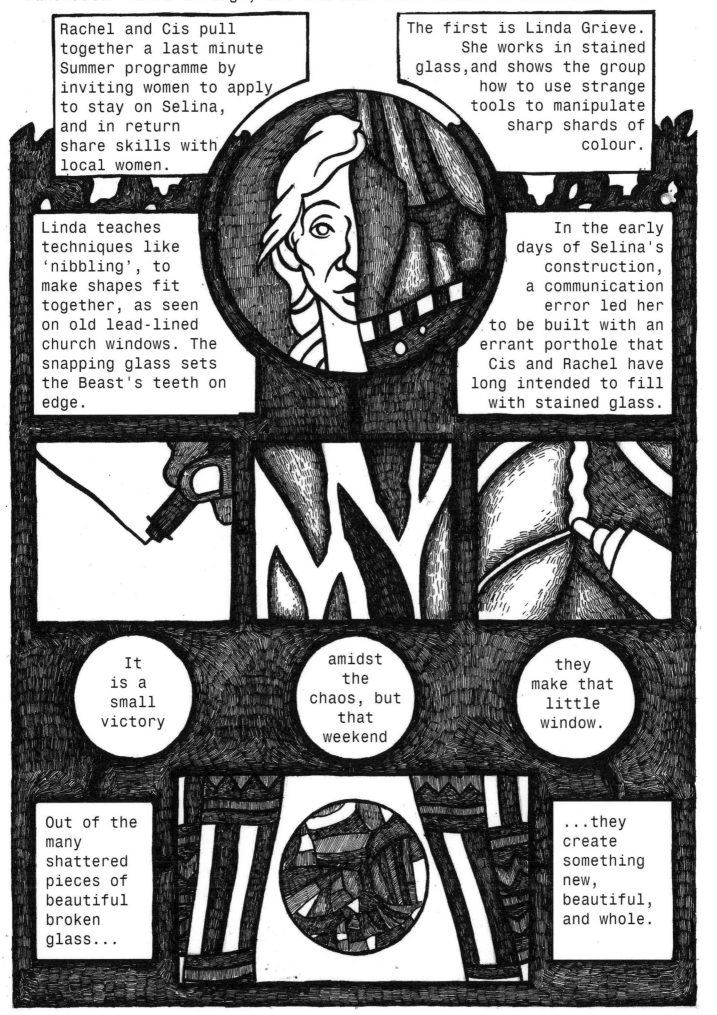

It is a small victory

amidst the chaos, but that weekend

they make that little window.

Out of the many shattered pieces of beautiful broken glass...

...they create something new, beautiful, and whole.

The next woman is Janette Scott, who shares her knowledge of environmental portraiture with the women gathered on Selina.

Janette gives a short lecture on early photography techniques, which those present absorb with evident enthusiasm, joy and wonder.

There is a magic to this. A free place to come and run amok. But also to learn new skills shared without the institutional hierarchy.

Janette is new to this herself, but is generous with her knowledge. Using phones and small digital cameras, she encourages the women to have fun with the medium.

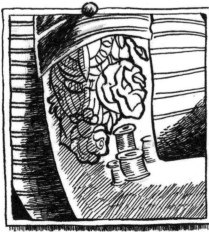

There are new women showing up for the workshops.

Some familiar faces too.

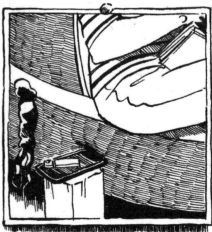

All of them enjoying the anarchy of each other's company.

In July, Raksha Patel makes a welcome return. She and the Beast decide to go to Shibden Hall in Halifax, the estate of the infamous Anne Lister. Both Raksha and the Beast catch their buses by a cat's whisker.

Raksha went to the opening of Howard Hodgkin's exhibition at The Hepworth, Wakefield. His paintings depicting India are showing as part of 'UK India Year of Culture'.

Raksha is angry and disappointed that they chose to shine the spotlight on a white Englishman's impressions of India, when they could have used the opportunity to exhibit work by an Indian or British Indian artist.

This aside, the week on Selina has had its good moments. Raksha managed to find a subject to sit for a portrait. A woman who owns a fabric shop in Savile Town. She's hoping to start a new series of portraits documenting South Asian women in the industrial North. But the canal has had a soporific effect, and she feels like she hasn't achieved enough.

Once they reach Halifax, Raksha and the Beast only get a little bit lost looking for the road to Shibden Hall.

The afternoon is gloriously sunny and warm, and the fields they pass are all insect buzz and Summer blooms.

Anne Lister is famous for being a female entrepreneur and adventurer.

And infamous for being a lesbian, and keeping a coded sex diary. The 1800s were wild.

A coal mine owner and savvy business woman, Lister's impressive Tudor mansion and gardens are a testament to her wealth and influence.

Museum guides are usually pretty amazing, and Dodi is no exception. She not only has extensive knowledge of Anne Lister and the house...

But the Hall features prominently in her personal history, having grown up just down the road.

Lister died while travelling, and never got to see the completion of her beloved library.

Raksha is understandably disappointed that Lister embraced some of the more chauvinistic traits that came with inhabiting a 19th century male role. But while Lister's rich, white privilege cannot be discounted, when she proclaimed 'intellect has no gender', it was a bold statement for a woman to make at that time

Raksha is followed by Sheree Angela Matthews.

Sheree describes herself as a 'creatrix', and is the supreme champion of creative practice as a survival skill.

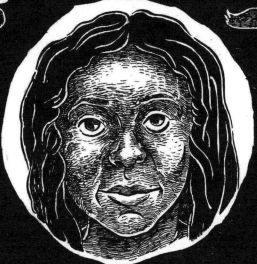

When the Beast meets her at Selina to hand over the keys, they find a family of ducklings stuck on the wrong side of the lock. Don't worry, they were all fine and totally adorable.

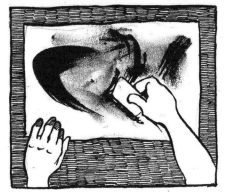

Sheree teaches the women to make their own sketchbooks.

And although the process feels like anarchy.

The result is as precise as a ritual.

Sheree's methods turn the catastrophic into the beautiful, and the innocuous into the fierce. Her work is political too. She collects a lot of magazines and brochures for collage, and often makes pieces critiquing the overwhelming whiteness of advertising.

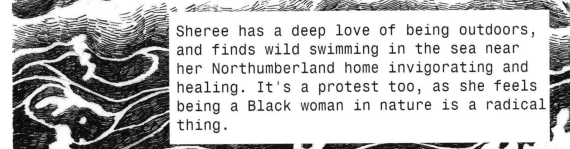

Sheree has a deep love of being outdoors, and finds wild swimming in the sea near her Northumberland home invigorating and healing. It's a protest too, as she feels being a Black woman in nature is a radical thing.

In July, Idle Women return to Coldwell and those transcendental Lancashire sunsets; this time, with the women of Humraaz.

When the Beast arrives, Cis and Rachel have taken some of the women and children on their first nature walk. An intense experience for anyone who hasn't grown up in or around the countryside.

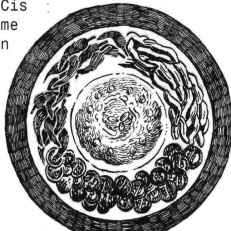

But before long they have lost their trepidation, and it's all Cis and Rachel can do to keep up and get them all home in time for dinner.

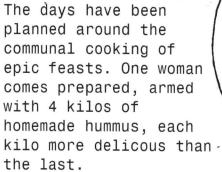

The days have been planned around the communal cooking of epic feasts. One woman comes prepared, armed with 4 kilos of homemade hummus, each kilo more delicous than the last.

On the first evening, the Beast notes three distinct groups: the grown-ups, who are quiet and a little unsure, often retreating to their rooms for breaks or to take care of very small children. The teenagers, in their own performative orbits, a species unto themselves. And the inexhaustible maelstrom of the under 12s.

By the second day, everyone has settled in. They've found their rhythm and everything feels more relaxed.

The Beast meets Ruby, who is working with Humraaz while in the early stages of a PhD. She is researching Pakistani Muslim women's journeys out of domestic violence in the U.K. There is little existing research on the subject, and as a result she's quickly becoming the expert in this field. Ruby is also working with Hyndburn and Ribble Domestic Violence Team, and the Wish Foundation.

Through these organisations, Ruby hopes to interview women and investigate and document the vulnerabilities specific to this community. These include socio-cultural norms relating to gender, social isolation, lack of knowledge of available services and language barriers.

Ruby identifies some of the forms of violence particular to these women:

Dowry and forced marriage.

Transnational abandonment.

Domestic servitude and honour-based violence.

Later, using clay and scraps of nature they've collected on walks, the women lose themselves in making the elements of a shared journey. Peace descends over Coldwell.

There is a BBQ feast that evening of royal proportions. And then it's time to build the bonfire.

Again, for many this will be a first, and the children scatter like loose marbles to collect firewood.

As the sun goes down, someone says she can almost hear the muezzin.

Another woman observes that this is one of things she misses most about home: communal cooking and eating.

One of the Humraaz women says that a new government strategy for dealing with the lack of space in shelters, will be to get women into houses as quickly as possible.

As practical as this sounds, it also increases feelings of isolation and helplessness that often cause women to go back to abusers, or toxic family situations.

Humraaz believes that for women to survive and thrive outside the shelter, they need solidarity and community.

Earlier in the evening, some of the kids put little tealights along the path that leads back to the activity centre. The effect this has on the darkened woods is one of enchantment.

The Beast passes out of the communal world of firelight and marshmallows and into the cool, blue, solitary Lancashire night.

The Beast sees two women that weekend who have the woods in their hearts.

Both their journeys are difficult and lonely, the paths often obscured.

One has been in the dark for some time.

But, while the trees still press close, the canopy over her head has begun to thin.

The dappled light is almost reminiscent of Spring.

The other stands at the edge of a thicket.

There are multiple tracks, but they are confused, and sometimes too vague to follow.

But despite this, there is magic in this deep Winter wood...

...and if she can find it, she will emerge more powerful than when she went in.

The Beast thinks about her own body, cis-gendered and comfortable, and what it means to inhabit it.

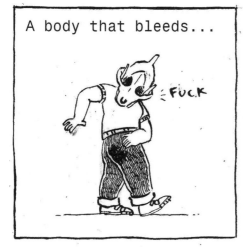

A body that bleeds...

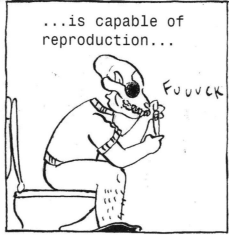

...is capable of reproduction...

...and commits chemical warfare against her once a month.

It is a woman's body when viewed through a binary lens in terms of:

Sex... "Your breasts look great in that shirt."

(burn this shirt)

...gender...

"Ha ha! She looks like a bloke!"

(burn that man)

... and violence.

"I was walking along the canal ..."   "That's very dangerous for a woman..."

The Beast wants to BURN IT ALL DOWN, manifesting her frustrations as a monster to fight with.

When she imagines herself, she sees a a joyful, sensory being, growing all her hair long and living out in the woods.

But the monster shouts back at her that she is nothing but biological functions, and a history of oppression.

The Beast knows that this it not true, and that there are more dissenters like her, hidden in the dark.

They are teaching her new ways of talking about sex, gender and violence, and together they will overthrow the dangerous, oppressive, dominant ideologies.

Without a consistent artist in residence on Selina holding Idle Women together, Cis and Rachel, and the Beast begin to drift apart over the Summer.

The Beast meets Rachel who confides that she and Cis are feeling the pressure of keeping on top of touring Selina, whilst working on 'Bricks and Mortar' in St Helens.

'Bricks and Mortar' demands a consistent presence from Rachel and Cis, because of the very vulnerable women.

It is sensitive work that requires very clear commitments, which you must be strict about honouring

"If you say 'See you next week' you have to mean it." Rachel says, but these are precisely the kind of promises she and Cis feel like they're breaking.

The Beast also tells Rachel that she won't be coming with them to St. Helens. She will stay in Dewsbury and keep working on the graphic novel, while Cis and Rachel will go west to salvage the Autumn.

The women part ways on the corner of a persistently sunny street. The Beast goes one way and Rachel another, their horizons obscured by increasingly restless waters.

"Which way now?"

"I thought you knew!"

Alana Jelinek arrives in August, on a train that the Beast misses by waiting for her on the wrong platform. She drags a box full of hatchets, and despite living over twenty years in London, Australia still loops and curls through her accent.

Alana is an artist and anthropology sympathiser. Working with museums, she uses wood carving to address the colonial problems of their collections.

Over the next few days, she's going to be teaching women on the tow path how to carve a spoon.

The canal thrums with the hollow sound of axes splitting soft wood.

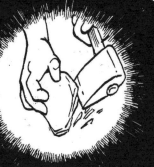

Spoons are coaxed out of watermelon scented sycamore.

The disaster everyone has been waiting for happens on the second day, when a woman drops an axe on her own foot. Rachel flies into action like a one-woman ambulance response unit, powered by the traumatic memory of Cis putting an axe through her hand a few years ago. Then the women go back to carving spoons.

The woman is a haemophiliac, of course.

But perhaps that's why she's so preternaturally calm.

A man walks past and says, 'You don't look very idle!' For the millionth time.

No-one even looks up. If an axe wound doesn't divert anyone's attention from spoon carving, a man doesn't stand a chance.

And then quite suddenly, it is the tail end of August. The evenings grow brass-coloured and chilly with Autumn's warning. The final workshop is banner making with Parveen.

Parveen encourages everyone to make their own protest sign. And although some struggle with their initial ideas, when the crafting gets underway, they're unstoppable.

Despite the troubled inception of Idle Women's improvised Summer programme, it has been a resounding success.

The next part of the tour remains unclear.The Beast makes a banner saying 'Everything is Terrible!'

Parveen embraces her first time as an 'Artist in Residence', and under her guidance the tow path erupts with cries of joy and rage.

A neon rally on the tow path where protest queens take up all of the space, unapologetically.

Rachel's banner causes controversy. A quote from Vi Subversa's '80s punk band Poison Girls (which she formed as a 44 year old mother of two), it later became a phrase their friend, Ray, would leave painted in places where she'd experienced some form of male violence.

One woman tells Rachel she thinks the quote is aggressive and sexist, but the Beast thinks the words 'self-defence' make it a clarion call for all the women killed or who kill as a result of male violence. If Rachel could have painted it on the side of Selina, she would.

Earlier that week, Parveen tells a shop owner in Dewsbury town centre to remove a t-shirt reading 'Wife Beater' from his window. Grudgingly he does so.

But it's back the next day.

While both designs allude to domestic violence, there's only one the Beast can imagine appearing on a novelty t-shirt in a shop window. And it isn't the one suffused with women's rage.

In early September, Nicky and Stella make a brief, but welcome return to Selina. It is a bittersweet homecoming.

There are many familiar faces. Heidi has given birth, and brings the new baby.

Rose has experienced some difficult shifts in her circumstances and is not in a good place.

One of the women is finally out of an abusive relationship, although the shadow of it still haunts her.

But for a few hours, Selina feels like she did in May.

Somewhere you can talk about addiction, recovery, parenting and cake.

The Beast leaves on a wave of laughter, the scent of baby powder and coffee following her into the early Autumn evening.

Throughout the year, Cis has continued her battle against the Black Root, a sickness which nearly consumed her and the entire project last Winter. Recently though, she had a revelation...

She dreamed she was sleeping in a tree, and slowly became aware that a tiger had climbed up there with her.

There was a group of people on the ground calling out warnings. She could feel their fear for her, terrified that the big cat would kill her.

But she remained calm.

She curled up against the tiger, and, even though she knew it could kill her at any moment, fell asleep again.

Through visualising the all-consuming exhaustion, Cis was able to transform it from something unknowable and ferocious, into a creature she could read and respond to.

"This is tansy, Tanacetum vulgare, traditionally used for abortion."

The tiger-dream conversation takes place in a little park just outside Dewsbury.

Afterwards, Cis, Rachel and the Beast walk around for a while.

"And this one's called James Roof!"

As they wander, the two women point out various plants to the Beast and tell her their names, which is a kind of healing all of its own.

There is an abundance of blackberries that season. Every bramble is 95% berry and 5% spiders. The Beast makes a pie.

Out of the blackberries... not the spiders.

That day, Idle Women's board of trustees have come to town to discuss Selina's future. The Beast walks from Dewsbury to Mirfield in bright Autumnal sunshine.

Ray greets her from the road near the marina.

The Beast sees women she met at the Shifting Loyalties Conference.

But there's trouble afoot that not even a pie can fix.

Idle Women have spent the Summer trying to work out how to get Selina to St. Helens, and where to put her once she's there. They were waiting to hear if they could crane her into a sliver of canal, but they can't get permission for the crane.

Now they must wait for planning permission to dry dock Selina on a traffic island. This location brings up all kinds of security issues and worries, but if they can't put her there, they won't be able to deliver the final part of the tour.

The Beast leaves the trustees talking softly of other things. The firelight recedes, and she walks the dark tow path with Stella, one last time.

Winter's chaos demon seems to have come back early as Idle Women's little family splits apart.

Rachel will go to St. Helens to continue delivering sessions to the women at the refuge.

Cis prepares to drive Adelaide to a marina they know in Accrington. Helen is going to Rachel's parents in Nottingham, and Selina will stay behind.

The boat's presence in Mirfield will be the one constant in an oily canal of doubt.

And a quiet reminder of all the magic that happened there.

AUTUMN 2017

St. HELENS, MERSEYSIDE

Since moving to Dewsbury, the Beast has been spending a lot of time with Arooje and Parveen. Today the 6-year old is arguing that she has learned everything.

"And that's why I never have to go back to school."

The Beast and Arooje's mum try to explain the importance of education and how being an adult has its down sides, but Arooje is having none of it.

Embracing the theme, Parveen asks:

"What's your favourite thing about being a grown-up?"

"Probably being able to make my own decisions."

But no sooner have the words left her mouth...

...then something cracks open in the Beast's mind...

...and she has the terrifying revelation that her autonomy...

...has very little to do with being an adult.

In the past, going out as a woman after curfew could lead to arrest. In the not too distant past, she wasn't allowed to vote. Even more recently, she wouldn't have been able to have a bank account or apply for a loan without a man's counter-signature. And let's not forget spousal rape only became a crime in the U.K. in 1991.

'When' the Beast was born is one thing, but 'where' is equally important, as a woman's autonomy differs around the world. Spatial and temporal luck at the accident of the Beast's birth has allowed her to live as she does, without being burned as a witch.

The least the Beast can do is be part of the cohort fighting for others' rights; holding the door open and making the space for those who still aren't being treated with the dignity and autonomony that should be a human right.

The next day at 8:50am sharp, Cis leaves the house. She is going to get the keys to the shop from the council today, come hell or highwater.

After a frustrating couple of hours, she relents, and calls the (male) director of Idle Women's partner in St. Helens.

She gets the keys.

They now have access to the shop. When Dina and Rachel pull up in the cantankerous Land Rover, the momentum of these small victories stirs them into action. They have two days to prepare the empty space.

Although Idle Women want the shop to be permanent, the initial promise gifts it to the women of St.Helens for three years.

But after the ethereal nature of Selina, this feels like an incredible opportunity to sink some real roots.

With the potential for a permanence that Idle Women were never able to feel on the water.

This Autumn, Idle Women are working with Croatian artist Dina Rončević, who has already had to roll with some of the punches in St Helens.

Dina's initial remit was to teach mechanics and welding by deconstructing the Land Rover, and rebuilding it into a dystopian future sci-fi vehicle.

But since time is now ruled by chaos demons, she's had to scale back her ambitions a little.

Cis and Rachel reassure Dina that they have no expectations, and whatever classes she's able to deliver will be enough.

Dina started out in animation, but the industry was exploitative and insecure. So...

...she became a mechanic, but the sexism in garages made it impossible to get a job.

Then she became a welder. An industry plagued by perhaps even more chauvinism and harassment.

Like a true artist, Dina took everything she'd learned and circled it back into her creative practice. Playing on Croatia's predominantly male 'Rat Bike' culture, she devised the 'Ratess' project.

She bought a wrecked motorbike and using everything she learned through her welding and mechanic training, taught a teenage girl to rebuild and ride it. The girl kept the bike with the promise that she would pass the skills onto another girl.

The bulding in St. Helens will become the Idle Women Institute. It will hold the workshops that should have been on Selina.

Saturday afternoons will be given over to survival skills, learned together from online tutorials and knowledge sharing.

The first session is lock picking, in honour of all the doors Rachel and Cis wish they could have broken open over the last few days.

And they have their first St. Helens attendee, Sheri.

Future workshops will cover urban foraging for Winter remedies.

Beard-making and disguises.

And perhaps even coding in the ambitious and hopeful future.

We all patiently manipulate pins in locks. Then halfway through the session, Cis comes in looking like Marley's ghost.

And everyone gets a turn with the bolt cutters.

Locks are sprung...

...chains are cut...

...and all the doors are left open for others to follow to freedom.

The Beast paints the sign for the Idle Women Institute.

Taking her inspiration from the wealth of heraldry she's found in Yorkshire and Lancashire, she devises a coat of arms.

Borage, for its hardiness and beauty, and its medicinal and edible qualities. This plant has long been associated with Idle Women. And a bee, the symbol of communal work and industry.

As mottos: the first is one the Beast has heard many times over the last few years, which always evokes power and hope.

The second, is for all those who embrace the dystopias they live in now, as sites alive with potential for change.

SURVIVE & THRIVE

IN DYSTOPIA WE TRUST

Central to the design is the Hammer and the Herb.

The hammer, to smash the white supremacist capitalist patriarchy.

And the herb, for lost knowledge, and the natural systems we must realign with.

AND HELEN   BECAUSE HELEN

Due to changes in funding, many independent and specialist domestic violence shelters are in danger of closing, yet demand for these services is at its highest.

The first domestic violence shelter was founded in Chiswick in London by Erin Pizzey in 1971. Not only did she make a safe space for women to run to, but, for the first time, she gave them the dignity of being believed.

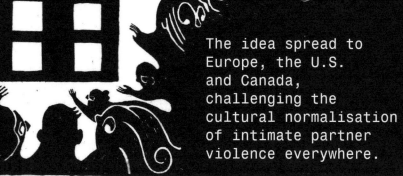

The idea spread to Europe, the U.S. and Canada, challenging the cultural normalisation of intimate partner violence everywhere.

Budgets shrink ...

violence reaches epidemic levels ...

women are housed in hostels and B'n'Bs...

unable to cope with those who have complex needs...

nothing for those with no recourse to public funds...

discrimi- nation against LGBTQ+ ...

...a service in crisis.

The difference between the two refuges the Beast has seen whilst working with Idle Women is palpable. An independent, well-resourced specialist service, catering to the specific needs of its users, as opposed to homogenised, oversubscribed, understaffed, unsafe, temporary housing available to others.

It shouldn't have to be this way. 'State-run' should not equate to 'poor', and surviving and thriving should not mean depending on charity.

The government chooses austerity. They choose to force the most vulnerable into the most volatile situations. Though we should fight to eliminate domestic violence, its causes and effects, we must in the meantime demand better from our institutions.

178

Dina is in her element. Cis and Rachel have entrusted her with the task of kitting out the Institute with the tools and equipment she'll need for the mechanics classes. The excitement of it sends Dina's own imagination into overdrive, and she tells of her plans for a building in the verdant Croatian countryside.

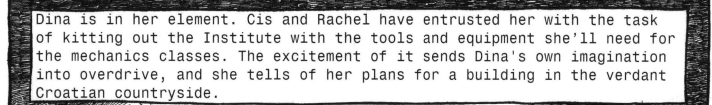

A whole complex dedicated to teaching mechanical skills to women and girls...

...where they won't have to put up with...

...all the sexism and misogyny that plagued her training and subsequent employment.

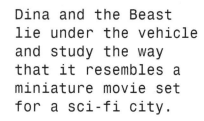

Dina and the Beast lie under the vehicle and study the way that it resembles a miniature movie set for a sci-fi city.

Then Dina's student arrives and it's time for the class to begin.

The woman brings her children, and Rachel and the Beast try and keep them from breaking into the workshop to learn mechanics with their mum.

Many of the women will be bringing young children to the sessions. Just looking after these two little souls is a handful, and Idle Women realise a play worker will be essential.

November is a time of rejection.

Now that the 'On The Water' tour is finishing, and 'Bricks and Mortar' is underway, Idle Women must start the long process of securing more funding for the coming year and beyond.

So far they've been turned down for everything they've applied for.

On the Beast's last day in St. Helens, Idle Women hear that they were turned down by Rosa, the organisation set up after the Tampon Tax came in, to allocate funds to women-led projects: an appeasement for the bleeding womb, being taxed on their own blood.

Idle Women aren't angry that someone else was awarded the funding...

they are livid that, on the day the successful projects are announced, it also comes to light ...

that £250,000 of the money not being assigned through Rosa, is going to the charity Life...

which is both anti-choice, and anti-sex education in schools.

To be eligible for Rosa's funding, the project had to be woman-led, with a majority of female trustees, and actively working for the benefit of women and girls.

Life meets none of those criteria, so basically the Tampon Tax is not only not helping women and girls (period poverty is a serious problem for some who bleed), it is funding organisations that actively do them harm.

Samhain comes around again.

And it feels very strange not to be on the tow path.

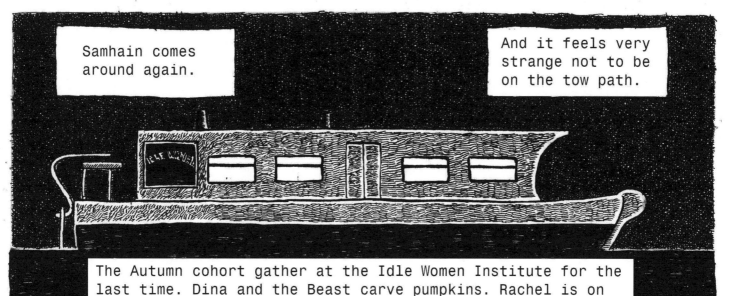

The Autumn cohort gather at the Idle Women Institute for the last time. Dina and the Beast carve pumpkins. Rachel is on the phone planning the next Shifting Loyalties Conference, and Cis is shaming a bus company for discriminating against one of the women they've been working with.

The Idle Women Institute is everything Selina couldn't be.

Accessible, multi-purpose, stable, and with potential...

...for women to have real ownership of.

These are the hopeful possibilities the Institute embodies. There will be challenges; setting and enforcing boundaries, having a visible presence, meeting the needs of those who access it.

But, compared to this time last year, when Rachel and Cis weren't even sure Idle Women would survive, let alone thrive for another year, it is exciting to have even a difficult future ahead.

Selina is set to remain in Mirfield for the foreseeable future, and, with nowhere she really needs to be while finishing the book, the Beast offers to stay on her. Cis and Rachel spend an afternoon teaching her how to look after the boat, including pushing her across the canal to the marina in order to get water or pick up coal deliveries.

It's a complex set of manoeuvres.

Which at first go very well.

Until she finds herself holding the wrong rope.

The Beast panics and jumps back onto Selina, but doesn't quite make it, and her leg is touching gross canal water.

She thinks of all the women she's met over the years, and how they managed not to fall into the canal.

Then she remembers Helen and her little life jacket, and her inelegant forays into accidental canal exploration.

She acknowledges a wet-footed affiliation with the little demon; and doesn't feel so bad.

Over the last two years,
Selina Cooper has transformed the canal,
from somewhere women are told is unsafe, to
a bold and nurturing place. Here, women have
developed new skills, plotted, organised and
thrived. They have learned to light fires
for warmth, and for revolution...

Selina was a site of
gathering and resistance. She was a sabbat.
She took up space unapologetically, and
transformed it into something powerful.
And she is a battleship-grey clarion call
for you to do the same.

Afterword

After *On The Water* ended many of the women on our journey talked of a painful absence, of how they never went back to the canal, and missed being close to nature and something deeper. So in 2018 we crowdfunded to purchase a small parcel of land alongside the Leeds and Liverpool Canal in Nelson, a few streets away from where the suffragist Selina Cooper lived and worked. This land, which Idle Women and Humraaz own together, is being transformed with women to become the UK's first physic or 'medicinal' garden dedicated to women and girls. The *Selina Cooper* narrowboat is moored alongside the garden, in the neighbourhood of her namesake, offering a new space to belong.

Humraaz continue to support women to flee male violence and transform their lives. The women of Humraaz we met on this tour continue to navigate ways around impossible obstacles, and to thrive. Friendships strengthen, and together we reach for something beyond the limits of the horizon.

The Idle Women Institute in St Helens continued to offer a space for women to dismantle the patriarchy until the Summer of 2019, when it became and remains, the offices of our touring partner. Before Idle Women left, women travelled from far and wide to create *Power Tools* – an online series of 14 DIY films, which are permanently available to all women.

Mojisola Adebayo completed writing her play *Stars*, which she began writing with Mae C Jemison on the *Selina Cooper*. *Stars* is published in *Mojisola Adebayo Plays Two*, and will soon be making its way to theatres and festivals.

Silvia Federici completed her book, *Witches, Witch-Hunting, and Women*, a pocket-sized revisiting of *Caliban and the Witch*; and she continues to make us feel connected to something powerful and hopeful. Ireland's Eighth Amendment is now history, with women still campaigning for the same rights in Northern Ireland; and Jesse Jones's installation *Tremble Tremble* has been exhibited at Talbot Rice Gallery in Edinburgh and the Guggenheim Museum Bilbao.

Dina Rončević of course succeeded in her vision to dismantle a Landrover Defender, and went on to teach women how to weld the parts into something new and dystopian. As far as we know, Candice 'the Beast' Purwin never fell into the canal again, and is working on new material, developing drawings for animation, and continuing to wander with curiosity through untrod landscapes.

Martina Mullaney, her daughter and their dog; and Stella Barnes and Nicky Bashall moved to Yorkshire to keep in close contact with the rivers and hills. To celebrate her half-century, Karen Mirza became Noor Afshan Mirza and moved onto a canal boat.

Arooje continues to teach us how to be wise and have fun, and Parveen Butt and Ray continue to support Idle Women as trustees. Ray is also collaborating with Idle Women on *Petrichor: a proposal for land*, our new site-specific performance project, made with older lesbians.

Alana 'the hatchet' Jenilek bought a motorbike and joined the infamous Dykes on Bikes. Sheree Angela Matthews has become a popular expert on using drills, and Raksha Patel is still the best fine art painter we know, and she's quite good at decorating too.

The mural of Mojisola's *A to Z of Women's Pleasure*, painted by Raksha and forty other women on the wall of the derelict staple factory at Church in Accrington remained untouched for a few years, even after the rest of the building was demolished. Riffat Batool and Riaz Begum founded the Idle Women Sisterhood, and continue to welcome us into their all-embracing family.

In case you were wondering, Helen is still with us, living out her retirement in extreme comfort on land, though she still partakes in occasional wild swimming.

Idle Women On the Water tells of just some of the 1800 women we met on our tour through Lancashire, Yorkshire and Merseyside. Although we don't reflect on them all here, each woman is held dearly; her courage, kindness and creativity is as essential to this story as the pages it is printed on.

On this fifth anniversary of Idle Women, we look back with a humbled perspective and compassionate understanding of the difficult task we set ourselves. So far, Idle Women has been a journey of self-discovery for us all: a painful lesson in self-worth, a training ground for choosing battles, and in caring for ourselves in the battles we have no choice in joining.

More than ever, we understand that public space remains male space and women's access to it is conditional, with safety never guaranteed. Whilst women continue to experience systemic violence, there will only be moments of beauty, but we believe these moments culminate and grow, and are worth fighting for.

Our determination to create sustainable space for women to belong on their own terms is stronger than ever, and we look forward to meeting you again in 2025 with the story of our next venture, to claim women's rightful place on the land. It will be a story that begins at the end of a slow and watery journey on the water.

Rachel Anderson and Cis O'Boyle
Accrington, August 2020

Candice Purwin

Candice Purwin writes and draws comics, and sometimes animates things. She is usually based somewhere in the UK, often under a desk or atop a shelf where humans are few and far between. She takes commissions and writes good letters.

www.candicepurwin.com

Acknowledgments

From Candice Purwin

The 'Beast' would like to thank, in no particular order, Parveen and Arooje for giving me a space to work and all the best food and conversation. Tess Mitchell and Ross Kilgour who put up with me getting up at 5:30am to ink pages before breakfast and Sean Jacquemain who put up with me wedged on his kitchen counter, also inking pages before breakfast. Lynsey Sutherland who lent me a studio. Maddie Breeze who gave me counsel. Everyone I met through the project, and the friendships and work that followed in subsequent years. Lastly, Selina Cooper for the sanctuary.

From Idle Women

On the Water was created through the kindness of many strangers who could imagine something different. Laurie Peake was the first person to say yes, and without her taking that risk we literally wouldn't be here. Salma Saleh reached out in the dark and took our hands; without her, we would still be wandering along the tow paths. Silvia Federici's friendship and courage reminds us of the broad history of women's resistance, to keep perspective, and to work for deeper transformation.

To our families, those who came before us, and those who joined us along the way through the best and the worst of times, you have taught us about belonging. Diane and Helen Jayne, thank you for the yellow moped and the music. Special thanks to Carol, Cheryl and Malcolm whose support, unyielding capacity and love, was with us before we began.

Thank you to old and new friends who generously gave ideas, criticality, courage and cheer; to those who raged, grieved, shouted and celebrated with us. And to the men who supported us and stepped aside, thank you.

Residents and collaborating artists

Silvia Federici
Liza Fior, Siw Thomas, Mara Kanthak
– muf architecture/art
Martina Mullaney, Cecile, and
Max the dog
Mojisola Adebayo
Noor Afshan Mirza
Nicky Bashall
Stella Barnes
Dina Rončević
Raksha Patel
Sarah Cole
Michelle Wren
Linda Grieve
Janette Scott
Alana Jenilek
Parveen Butt
Sheree Angela Matthews
Nancy Barrett
Karen Shannon
Natalie Deighton
Anisa
Safina Sajid
Riffat Batool
Riaz Begum
Moya O'Hagan
Dana Popa
Ruth Ewan
Jesse Jones
Sarah Brown
Mina Said-Allsopp
Natasha Gordon
Deni Francis
Crin Claxton
Jacqui Beckford
Alison Pottinger
Charlie Folorunsho
Rahila Gupta
Rehana Zaman
Uzma Kasi
Jean McEwan
Alberta Whittle
Laura Salisbury

Irish Artist Collective
Annette Mees
Yara El-Sherbini
Davina Drummond
Katie Jean
Selina Papoutseli
Wendy Burnett
Mama D
Claire Heuchan
Sonia Dyer
Boseda Olawoye
Dedj Leibbrandt
Lizzie Linton
Anna Smith
Charmian Griffin
Fatema Abdoolcarim
Leyla Hussein
Louise Robertson
Sorrel Weaver
Max Dashu
Jashmin Patel
Ikamara Larasi
Kajal Nisha Patel
Dervela McNee
Eileen Leahy
Suneeda Maruthiyil
Jill Jennings
Cheryl Anderson
Eleanor Phillips

Humraaz Partnership

Firoza Mohmed
Salma Saleh
Fazarna Chand
Shamim Nawaz
Yasmin Namaji
Sue Hopkinson
Maryam Patel
Penelope D'Souza
Maira Butt
Mehmona Arif
Shakeela Miah.

All the women who can't be named

Building the *Selina Cooper* and Waterways support
Iolo & Mary SB Adieu & Nao NB Kingfisher for inspiration, preparation and courage
ABC Boats: Anne and her team
Swanley Bridge Marina : Mandy and Liz
Shone Boat Co. Ltd: Rob
Willow Boat Painting: Sally and her team
D and J Engineering: Danny
Croughton Narrowboat Services: Eric
Knotts Bridge Marina: Jill
Altham Marine Services
CV Marine and Shepley Bridge Marina: Angela and Gordon
Reedley Marina: Jon and Graham
Church, Accrington mooring: Linda and Dave Barber, Lynn

Touring partners
Super Slow Way Laurie Peake, Katie May, Ruth Shorrock, Laura Kelly and Zephie Begelo
Creative Scene Nancy Barrett, Vicky Holliday and Parveen Butt
Canal and River Trust Emma Fielding, Tim Eastop, Steven Higham and Tom Wright
Heart of Glass Kat Dempsey, Suzanne Dempsey Sawin, Sue Potts, Patrick Fox, Lindsey West and Laura Swithenbank

Organisations
Humraaz Support Services; Lancashire Women; Beacon Children's Centre; WomenCentre, Calderdale and Kirklees; MATCH Mothers: Mothers Apart From Their Children; Helena Refuge and Housing; Refugee Women Connect; St. Helens Mind; Imkaan (incl.Purple Drum); The Dahlia Project; Ali Collective; Bangor Street Community Centre; Eanam Wharf; The Bureau; In-Situ; Waterfall Mill; Rosegrove Library; Gannow Community Centre; Duke of Edinburgh Award at Little Deer Wood Activity Centre, Mirfield; Soroptimist International of Dewsbury; Whitehough Outdoor Centre; Coldwell Activity Centre; Kokoro Kickboxing; Blackburn Cobras ABC Boxing Club and Fitness Centre; Booths, Barrowford; Roy Cattermole Tree Sevices; Ribble Valley Log Supplies Ltd; Blackburn Super Women; Fair For All; Kutchi Women's Group; and UCLAN (University of Central Lancashire)

Idle Women Trustees
Kareema Ali
Adelaide Bannerman
Parveen Butt
Maria Caroll
Anna Hart
Alana Jelinek
Nao Nagai
Laurie Peake
Jill Raymond

PR Janette Scott
Current Idle Women branding and website O-SB Design
Original Idle Women branding and pamphlets Laura Salisbury
External supervision Dr Maeve Malley
External evaluation Lynn Froggett
Accountants Gill Davies and Courtney Wright

www.idlewomen.org

Funding
Idle Women On The Water was supported by Arts Council England Strategic Touring and delivered through partnerships with Super Slow Way, Creative Scene, Canal & River Trust and Heart of Glass. This publication has been produced using public funding by Arts Council England through the National Lottery.

191